THE COUNTRYSIDE IN BLOOM 1996

THIS BOOK BELONGS TO:

Hyacinth Bucket

BBC BOOKS

This book is published to accompany the television series entitled *Keeping Up Appearances*, series 5, first broadcast in Autumn 1995. The series was produced by BBC Television Executive Producer Harold Snoad

Published by BBC Books, an imprint of BBC Worldwide Publishing, BBC Worldwide Limited, Woodlands, 80 Woodlane, London W12 OTT

First published 1995
© Format and television scripts Roy Clarke, 1995
© This book Jonathan Rice, 1995
The moral right of the author has been asserted

ISBN 0 563 37186 2

Designed by Hammond Hammond
Handwriting by Graham Redfern
Illustrations by Chris Lloyd and Don Hagor
All photographs © BBC except page 41 Barnaby's Picture Library

Set in Simoncini Garamond,
Snell Roundhand Bold Script and Jansen Text
Printed and bound in Great Britain by
Butler and Tanner Ltd, Frome
Jacket printed by Lawrence Allen Ltd,
Weston-super-Mare

Colour reproduction by Radstock
Reproductions Ltd, Midsomer Norton

Calendars

1995

JANUARY	FEBRUARY	MARCH	APRIL
M T W T F S S	M T W T F S S	M T W T F S S	M T W T F S S

1996

JANUARY
M	T	W	T	F	S	S
1	2	3	4	5	6	7
8	9	10	11	12	13	14
15	16	17	18	19	20	21
22	23	24	25	26	27	28
29	30	31				

FEBRUARY
M	T	W	T	F	S	S
			1	2	3	4
5	6	7	8	9	10	11
12	13	14	15	16	17	18
19	20	21	22	23	24	25
26	27	28	29			

MARCH
M	T	W	T	F	S	S
				1	2	3
4	5	6	7	8	9	10
11	12	13	14	15	16	17
18	19	20	21	22	23	24
25	26	27	28	29	30	31

APRIL
M	T	W	T	F	S	S
1	2	3	4	5	6	7
8	9	10	11	12	13	14
15	16	17	18	19	20	21
22	23	24	25	26	27	28
29	30					

MAY
M	T	W	T	F	S	S
		1	2	3	4	5
6	7	8	9	10	11	12
13	14	15	16	17	18	19
20	21	22	23	24	25	26
27	28	29	30	31		

JUNE
M	T	W	T	F	S	S
					1	2
3	4	5	6	7	8	9
10	11	12	13	14	15	16
17	18	19	20	21	22	23
24	25	26	27	28	29	30

JULY
M	T	W	T	F	S	S
1	2	3	4	5	6	7
8	9	10	11	12	13	14
15	16	17	18	19	20	21
22	23	24	25	26	27	28
29	30	31				

AUGUST
M	T	W	T	F	S	S
			1	2	3	4
5	6	7	8	9	10	11
12	13	14	15	16	17	18
19	20	21	22	23	24	25
26	27	28	29	30	31	

SEPTEMBER
M	T	W	T	F	S	S
						1
2	3	4	5	6	7	8
9	10	11	12	13	14	15
16	17	18	19	20	21	22
23	24	25	26	27	28	29
30						

OCTOBER
M	T	W	T	F	S	S
	1	2	3	4	5	6
7	8	9	10	11	12	13
14	15	16	17	18	19	20
21	22	23	24	25	26	27
28	29	30	31			

NOVEMBER
M	T	W	T	F	S	S
				1	2	3
4	5	6	7	8	9	10
11	12	13	14	15	16	17
18	19	20	21	22	23	24
25	26	27	28	29	30	

DECEMBER
M	T	W	T	F	S	S
						1
2	3	4	5	6	7	8
9	10	11	12	13	14	15
16	17	18	19	20	21	22
23	24	25	26	27	28	29
30	31					

1997

JANUARY	FEBRUARY	MARCH	APRIL
M T W T F S S	M T W T F S S	M T W T F S S	M T W T F S S

Notes

Useful Telephone Numbers:

Accountant — 01252 234433

Solicitor — *Unnecessary in a well-organised life*

Bank — 01252 270370 *Funny little woman with large teeth and a smile —Linda?*

Police Station — 01252 313380 *The sergeant has a moustache*

Taxi — 01252 341025 *Call early—they take forever to arrive.*

Railway Station — 01252 371329 *The station master is never there.*

Travel Agent — 01252 512190 *(they have the best brochures)*

Post Office — 01252 613183 *(to divert mail when necessary)*

Electrician — 01252 623710 *(dirty hands—must not touch wallpaper)*

Plumber — 01252 702096 *(does not always shave—and wears an ear-ring!)*

Florist — *C.P. Benedict*

Useful Information:

National Health Insurance No: *We're private*

Driving Licence No: *Richard drives—it's so much more comfortable*

Passport Number:

In Case of Emergency:

Contact — *Richard Bucket Esquire*
The Residence

Doctor — *Typical!*

Note: Whilst every effort has been made to ensure the accuracy of the information contained in this diary, the publishers cannot accept responsibility for any changes or errors that may occur.

CANDLE LIGHT SUPPER with full silver service. January 9th, 7.30 for 8.

Menu: Prawn cocktail (there's an 'r' in the month, after all)
Roast beef of old England.
Carrots, red cabbage (is that a Communist dish? Probably not now the Berlin wall is down)
Fruit salad (including kiwi fruits and pineapple)
Bath Oliver Biscuits and English cheese (Cheddar, Double Gloucester, Wensleydale)
Hand thrown after dinner mints.
Real coffee in dear Mummy's best cups.

SUPPER OF THE CHINESE CANDLES. February 9th, 7.30 for 8.

Menu: Chinese prawn cocktail
Roast beef of old Shanghai
Carrots, red peppers, bean sprouts
Sweet and sour fruit salad (inc. lichees and water chestnuts)
Water Biscuits and cheese (do the Chinese make cheese? I fear not)
Hand thrown after dinner mints
China tea in dear Mummy's best cups.

TUSCAN TEMPTATION ALFRESCO, 25th May at Marston Hall 12.30 for 1.

Menu: ~~Pappardelle al Sugo di Arrosto, Insalata di Fagioli Bortotti~~
~~Acqua Cotta, Rabbit St. Angelo, Pigeon In Olives~~
Ravioli
Carrots, cauliflower
Dry Biscuits and Parmesan cheese
Italian ice cream
Hand thrown after dinner mints
Cappucino coffee (in dear Mummy's best cups).

OUTDOORS INDOORS LUXURY BARBECUE, 29th June, 7.30 for 8

Menu: Mixed grill (lamb chops, none of those horrible hamburger things)

  Beef steaks
  Carrots
  Biscuits and cheese
  English strawberry ice cream
  Hand thrown after dinner mints
  Real coffee (in dear Mummy's best cups)

ART APPRECIATION EVENING with Finger Buffet, 24th August, 7.30 for 8.

Menu: Finger Buffet
  Hand thrown after dinner mints
  Real coffee (in dear Mummy's best cups)

MERRIE ENGLAND BARBECUE, at Marston Hall, 22nd September, 7.30 for 8.

Menu: Merrie England is much the same as Outdoors Indoors. It worked so well last time.

CHRISTMAS EVE FAMILY DINNER, 24th December, 7.30 for 8

Menu: Prawn cocktail
  Roast turkey with all the trimmings
  Carrots, Brussels sprouts, broad beans
  Biscuits and cheese
  Christmas pudding, brandy butter and ice cream
  Hand thrown after dinner mints
  Coffee (can I trust Onslow with Mummy's best cups?)

NEW YEAR'S EVE   SUNDAY 31

A brand new year, and a brand new diary. I've never really been one for keeping diaries in the past, as I have never seen the need to write down one's triumphs, especially when other people seem to find out about them anyway. This year will be different, though, because Richard gave me a wonderful decorative diary as a little extra Christmas present. Waste not, want not, as dear Mummy used to say, a philosophy that I have always tried to follow, even though Daddy never quite got the hang of it

NEW YEAR'S DAY-HOLIDAY   MONDAY 1

My New Year's Resolution is the same this year as every year: to bring an oasis of culture and good taste to our community. I am sure I will succeed. I always do.

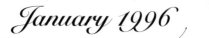

2 TUESDAY

Richard is outside, merrily cleaning the car, so I am taking the opportunity to plan my first 'At Home' of the year. We shall start with simplicity itself: a plain Candle Light Supper with full silver service and hand-thrown after dinner mints, a soirée that tells everyone that simple elegance is in fashion for another year. Tuesday 9th I will mark it in my diary now.

3 WEDNESDAY

Invitations sent to the Major and Mrs. Wilton-Smythe, Mr. and Mrs. Millburn, (he's the Frosticles king) and of course Elizabeth and Emmet. Where would their social life be without me to bring them into society?

4 THURSDAY

Replies received from the Millburns, who are unavailable. Frosticles are receiving the Queen's Award! My Candle Light Supper comes second only to a Royal occasion! Major Wilton-Smythe says yes but his wife has claustrophobia. Of course Elizabeth and Emmet will come. I need three more guests.

FRIDAY 5

Shall I tell Elizabeth to come on her own, to make the numbers equal, and then I could also invite Mrs. Councillor Nugent and her husband? No. Emmet so looks forward to discussing music and other artistic matters with me. It would not be fair

SATURDAY 6

Twelfth Night. The season of goodwill is over. Richard took down the Christmas decorations including the wreath with holly berries on the front door, and the Christmas tree topped by the beautiful angel that Sheridan made for his Mummy from half a Rice Krispies packet and some cotton wool at his kindergarten. It brings back such happy memories of my little boy whose skills with cardboard boxes and sticky-back plastic even then set him apart from other children.

7 SUNDAY

Church. I wore my navy hat with a hint of a veil. Richard wore the tie I gave him for Christmas. Emmet played the organ, but did not always get the tune right in all the hymns, so I felt obliged to lead the congregation towards the correct notes. Afterwards the vicar said he had never heard singing like it, which was most gratifying.

I have now invited the Barker-Finches, but they cannot come. Another engagement, they say. Rang Mrs. Councillor Nugent, but she has a council meeting. There's no reference to a council meeting in the local newspaper this week.

8 MONDAY

Mrs. Councillor Nugent said it was an emergency meeting called at very short notice, so it wouldn't have been in the local paper. There must be a crisis in government circles which we are not being told about.

Note: Ring Prime Minister concerning council crisis.

January 1996

Candle Light Supper with full silver service and hand-thrown after dinner mints. 7.30 for 8.00. But I am still three guests short. The Major arrived at 7.28, and Elizabeth and Emmet turned up at 7.42 (Elizabeth wearing that green outfit she likes so much). Then almost as if predestined by some evil fates, the doorbell rang at 7.49 and there were my three extra guests, Daisy, Rose and Onslow. They had come to tell me that Daddy is missing, on safari in pursuit of the milk lady. I had the choice of telling the assembled company about Daddy's regrettable hormone imbalance or of inviting my family to join us at the dinner table. As Onslow was wearing a shirt for a change, and the Major began to take a close interest in Rose, Richard and I let them stay.

Daddy is still missing, of course.

I have telephoned the Prime Minister's office, but was not given any useful information on the local government crisis, so I will have to get Richard to visit the town hall in due course.

0171 930 3050

12 FRIDAY

Daddy has returned. He refuses to say where he was. Could he have been called out of retirement to help the council in their time of crisis?

13 SATURDAY

To Marston Hall for the weekend.
To take: Water-colouring equipment including easel.
Jigsaws (the 1500 piece one of Renoir's 'Ships At Bay', the 500 piece vase of flowers, and the wooden one of a horse that Sheridan used so to love).
Best glasses. You never know who might drop in.
Second-best crockery. They won't stay for a meal.
Riding clothes? Country tweeds?
Richard must take three suits.
That's the beauty of having a place in the country. One can break with one's routine.

SUNDAY 14

Marston Hall. So many of my diary entries will be headed 'Marston Hall', our country pied-à-terre where so many of the best names in the county are now our dear neighbours. Perhaps I should illustrate the diary with some of my own impressions of the delicate mysteries of the countryside. I know I have inherited many of Daddy's skills in water-colouring. He was such a big noise in painting-by-numbers circles in his day: in fact, he was a big noise in almost every circle he got involved in, which is why Richard and I find it impossible to have him living with us at The Residence.

Raining. Cold. I cannot make the 'Ships At Bay' work, and the vase of flowers is missing half its pieces. I have

MONDAY 15

completed Sheridan's horse eighteen times. Richard thinks he is starting a cold.

Back at The Avenue. Richard definitely has a cold. He is not good company.

16 TUESDAY

Richard has given me his cold.

17 WEDNESDAY

It really is too bad of Richard to do this to me. This should have been my day to work at the charity shop, but I cannot go in this condition. Richard said that when he rang Mrs. Councillor Nugent, she told me to take all the time I need to make a full recovery, even though the shop can hardly operate without me. I expect her thoughts are distracted by the Council Crisis.

18 THURSDAY

I have now completed Sheridan's horse jigsaw seventy-six times.

My cold is turning into flu. Elizabeth, poor dear, has been most solicitous, but I expect she is missing our little morning get-togethers over a cup of coffee.

SUNDAY 28

I think the Council Crisis is still with us.
Un'd 's. Councillor Nugent could not come to the
then; phone when I rang to invite her to hear
given Ri sing for the Church old folk, which I have
woul th mised the vicar and Emmet I will do
look he y soon. We are definitely not being told
erything that we need to know.

He a — hould I enter politics and put things right?
pity
comp R
walk a
theu

Pages removed —
Richard spilt my
← breakfast yoghurt!
(Kindness itself,
but clumsy.)

MONDAY 29

I have discovered where I was going wrong
s.. Renoir's 'Ships at Bay'. It is 'Stags at Bay',
th r c d it is not by Renoir at all. It's a Canaletto.
trou I wondered where all the antlers were
dark supposed to go.
hai 1
sh.

30 TUESDAY

Rehearsing for the Church old folk. My 'Annie Get Your Gun' is still the favourite. Nobody can 'whip crack-away' the way I do. Emmet says accompanying me is a brand new musical experience every time. How sweet he is.

31 WEDNESDAY

A call from the vicar. My songs for the old folk will have to be postponed, as that nasty flu is going through them, and shocks would not do them any good. Oh well, more time to rehearse with Emmet.

1 THURSDAY

My next Candle Light Supper will be on Friday 9th, to coincide with Chinese New Year, which I understand occurs some time this month. It does seem very casual of the Chinese to begin their year six weeks late.

February 1996

Mr. and Mrs. Councillor Nugent are invited to my Supper of the Chinese Candles, and the Frosticle Millburns. He cannot be receiving another honour from Her Majesty already. And Elizabeth and Emmet. Emmet and I will entertain the company with extracts from 'Madam Butterfly' and 'Chu Chin Chow' to complete the Chinese atmosphere.

We went to Benedict's Garden Centre but did not bump into C.P. Benedict, Richard's dearest friend who owns it. Then on to Marston Hall.

4 SUNDAY

Daisy telephoned this morning. I was surprised to hear from her so early in the day, but apparently she had been up all night, as the house has been under siege.

"Under what?" I asked, for pearl-handled electronic telephones do not usually convey such brutal messages.

"Siege. S-I-E-G-E," she replied.

"Daisy, I know how to spell the word. Why are you under siege? Who is attacking you?"

"We think it might be Mrs. Acaster. Daddy did not treat her very well, you know," Daisy said.

"What has Mrs. Acaster been doing? Is Daddy safe?" I asked and Daisy replied, "Daddy's asleep. He's been asleep all night, even when the brick came through the window. It's me and Onslow who have suffered."

At that point there was a ring on Daisy's doorbell. I was reassured to learn that it was working again. I caught a muffled sound of raised voices in the distance and then Rose came to the telephone.

"That's all right then, Hyacinth. Don't worry," she said and she put the phone down. Don't worry! How can I not worry when Daddy's life is threatened by the vengeance of Mrs. Acaster? I tried to ring Daisy back again, but no reply.

5 MONDAY

Marston Hall. It is lovely here, but I do worry about Daddy. I tried to telephone Daisy again, but I could not get through. Either the phone lines have been cut and the siege is reaching its final stages, or Rose is talking to one of her boyfriends. There is nothing on the radio or television about the siege, so Richard says I am worrying too much.

TUESDAY 6

As soon as we got back from Marston Hall, Richard drove me round to Daisy's house. It is, of course, difficult to tell from the outside whether the house has been under siege or not, but Daisy was there to tell me that the siege is now over. It was not Mrs. Acaster, it was a Mr. Murchison proposing marriage to Rose, by attaching a ring to a large brick and throwing it at the house. Rose has not accepted, even though Mr Murchison has repaired the window. She has given him back his ring, and kept the brick.

WEDNESDAY 7

Bad news. The Millburns cannot attend my Supper of the Chinese Candles. There is a Frosticles International Seminar that day, whatever that is. Mr and Mrs. Councillor Nugent say they have another engagement that evening already, but I suspect she is merely trying to hide from us the severity of the Council Crisis.

THURSDAY 8

I have invited the Major and Mrs. Wilton-Smythe, but she suffers from sinophobia. I also invited the vicar, but he says that priests are not supposed to celebrate Chinese New Year. A directive from the bishop, apparently.

9 FRIDAY

Supper of the Chinese Candles. A success. Yes, a success as usual. The water chestnuts were a little hard, and Elizabeth spilled most of her food, but Daddy's pills are working, so we did not have any unexpected visits from the rest of the family.

10 SATURDAY

We met Miss Wilkinson in the High Street this morning.

"Happy New Year," I cried. "It's the Chinese New Year, you know. I think it's right to celebrate the festivals of all cultures, don't you?"

"Oh. Yes. Chinese New Year. We used to celebrate that in a big way when we lived in Hong Kong," said Miss Wilkinson. (Hong Kong indeed! I doubt if she's been farther east than Margate.) "Let's see. Which year is it this year?"

"1996," I said.

"No, No, I mean in the Chinese zodiac."

She looked pensive for a moment.

"It's the Year Of The Rat. Happy New Year."

How dare it be the Year Of The Rat! I have wasted a perfectly good Candle Light Supper celebrating the arrival of The Year Of A Rodent! You just can't trust these Orientals. I will never sing selections from 'Chu Chin Chow' again. The Year Of The Rat indeed. No wonder the vicar is not allowed to celebrate it.

A dull day. Rain, cold and Richard wandered around the house like a lost soul. He brushed against the flock wallpaper in the hall four times in just twenty minutes this morning. It is just too bad.

13 TUESDAY

A brighter day, but still cold. A brisk north-easterly wind which seemed to be worthy of the description 'bracing', and just right for playing golf in. Richard disagrees.

14 WEDNESDAY   ST. VALENTINE'S DAY

Daisy rang, rather dejected. The postman has delivered twenty-eight Valentine's cards to their house, twenty-five for Rose (of course), two for Daddy and one for Onslow. But none for Daisy. Daisy sent the one to Onslow, and Rose and Daisy sent the two to Daddy. Onslow does not believe in Valentine's cards, as a matter of philosophical principle, he says. A matter of idleness, say I. "He's so good at hiding all that passion in that lovely chest of his," was how Daisy expressed it, at which point I had to warn her to tone down the content of her conversation, which was possibly now exceeding the specification of our slimline touchtone telephone.

At our house, we do not receive Valentine's cards. They are all very well in some social spheres, I suppose, but they would not do for The Avenue.

Richard received a Valentine's card yesterday and he never told me about it! It was lucky I found it in the glove compartment of the car or I would never have known! Richard says it is a joke from his old office chums at the Council. No wonder there is a Crisis if they have nothing better to do than to make tasteless jokes at the expense of their former colleagues!

I sent Richard out to investigate the Council Crisis further. He was gone for several hours.

Marston Hall. Richard and I have decided to clean our weekend retreat from top to toe. Richard spent the afternoon moving furniture, while I polished our country silver.

Richard is looking tired. He is taking his retirement too seriously.

Valentine, you've captured my heart

18 SUNDAY

Marston Hall. Lent begins on Wednesday, so I have decided to make a list of what we intend to give up.

1. Sugar on our breakfast cereals, even those which are by appointment to the Royal Households of Scandinavia.
2. Doing the crossword after breakfast (Richard).
3.

I can't think of anything else. Our lives are abstemious enough already.

19 MONDAY

A telephone call from Sheridan! I knew when I was speaking to Daisy last week that he was trying to get through to me. Now after several days of trying he has succeeded.

He and his friend Tarquin are in Morocco. He needs a little money, which I have promised to send to him to pay for what he said was something to keep him warm at night. An embroidered Arab blanket I expect.

SHROVE TUESDAY   **TUESDAY** 20

I invited Elizabeth in for coffee and pancakes, but she refused to toss a pancake when I suggested she should join in the spirit of the day. Then she squirted lemon juice all over my new kitchen rug. Poor girl, all thumbs and nerves.

ASH WEDNESDAY   **WEDNESDAY** 21

My day at the Charity Shop. A very impolite woman took my hat from the peg on which I had carefully placed it and offered me £2 for it. It is one of my favourite blue creations, the one with a white rose set decoratively over the left ear. I told her very firmly it was not for sale, at which she asked how much for my coat. She then offered me five pounds for the complete ensemble. She did not remain long in the shop.

THURSDAY 22

Daddy has to go to the clinic for more of those pills. Richard has taken him. It keeps him from doing the crossword after breakfast, although actually he is not eating much breakfast these days.

23 FRIDAY

Daddy's pills are not working. He became far too friendly with the physiotherapist for a man of his social history, and the dose has had to be doubled. If he could take whatever Onslow uses, we would have no worries about hyper-activity.

24 SATURDAY

Marston Hall. Richard got down to more furniture moving, followed by a little hard polishing, while I rearranged the country crockery on the sideboard. How we both enjoyed it!

Marston Hall, our little rural retreat.

Marston Hall. A lovely early spring day, perfect for a drive in the country. Richard cleaned the car instead of doing the crossword, and we set out, but had hardly reached the end of our splendid driveway when the heavens opened. We turned round and came back immediately. Richard sat glumly at the window waiting for the rain to stop, presumably so that he could get outside and clean the car again.

Daisy rang. Do we know a new physio— therapist for Daddy, as his present one has just had a breakdown? I will put Richard on to it at once.

27 TUESDAY

Richard went out for several hours, and did not tell me where he had been. Has he been recalled by the Council to help with the Crisis?

28 WEDNESDAY

Daisy rang. She says the house is in turmoil, which comes as no great surprise to me or to anybody who has ever been inside the place. Rose is trying to decide who to propose to tomorrow, Leap Year Day. Mr. Butterfield is high on the list, apparently, as is Mr. Merryweather the kitchen fittings man, and Mr. Helliwell.

29 THURSDAY

(Leap Year!)

Rose proposed to Mr. Butterfield, then Mr Hepplewhite. They both turned her down, mainly on the grounds that they were married already. Mr. Hepplewhite said they did not need a piece of paper to prove their love. By mid-afternoon, Rose had proposed to seven or eight people, but as far as I can gather, she is still a single lady.

It does not look as though we shall have to announce the forthcoming marriage of Rose in the newspapers. Even Boris and the model aeroplane man have turned her down.

Marston Hall. Richard is showing some reluctance to stick to his Lenten resolutions. He says it's bad enough not being allowed to do the crossword, without being deprived of a teaspoonful of sugar on his cornflakes. "What's the point in waking up in the morning if all I have to look forward to is sour cornflakes and the births, marriages and deaths?" were his exact words. I pointed out that the births, marriages and deaths are the social hub of the newspaper, and if he switched to Frosticles, winner of a Queen's Award, he would not need extra sugar because it is one of the many wholesome ingredients listed on the side of the packet.

I fear Richard's religious convictions are wavering. Ring vicar for advice.

3 SUNDAY

Sunshine. I wore my purple and pink dress with my best pearls to celebrate the onset of spring. The vicar's sermon was about the glory of work. 'Man goeth forth to his work, and to his labour until the evening.' Richard cleaned the car this afternoon. Then it rained.

Richard's eyes are closed. And well they might be!

COSTLESS CASH AND CARRY

SHOE CLEANING KIT
TOTAL: £2.50

SALES SLIP 1190500

4 MON

It's Onslow's birthday on Wednesday. I suppose that means a party: the Bun-fight at the O.K. Corral again. Perhaps we should have given up being seen in public with Onslow for Lent.

TUESDAY 5

Brought Onslow a shoe cleaning outfit for his birthday. Several sensible shades of shoe polish, two brushes and a smart yellow duster, all contained in a crisp black leather case, which any man would be proud to own. Richard says it will not be much good for Onslow's trainers.

WEDNESDAY 6

Onslow's birthday. Our gift was a great success. Onslow has always wanted dark tan bedroom slippers, says Daisy, and Rose pointed out that Daddy could use the black polish as camouflage when he and Colonel Dawlish go on night sorties. Colonel Dawlish has been dead for at least thirty years, and anyway finished up a Brigadier General.

THURSDAY 7

The celebrations were held in a pub. Somebody of my status in local society should not associate with people who rarely wear shirts, so I did not attend. Richard insisted on representing the Buckets, and he returned in no state to be seen by Mr. Hislop at number 43. Onslow says anyway they pulled Richard out of the hedge before Mr Hislop at number 43 came out to investigate. I fear I must ring the vicar soon.

<u>cont.</u>

8 FRIDAY

Richard has a headache. He says it is a hang-over and he needs the fizzy tablets which dissolve noisily in a glass of water, but I will not allow Richard to suffer from such a socially unfortunate condition.

9 SATURDAY

Richard's illness is an executive migraine, brought on by the years of responsibility at the Council offices. I told him maybe he can claim compensation for Repetitive Strain Syndrome. He says he thinks he could.

At last I managed to get hold of the vicar. I have explained that it must be kept entirely confidential, but Richard seems to be expressing Religious Doubts. The vicar said that Richard is a man with a heavy burden to carry, and it is not surprising if he experiences some dark nights of the soul. I explained that he had me to help him carry the burden, and the vicar said, "Exactly".

The vicar preached on the Patience of Job. "I hope the text of my sermon will help," he said to Richard as we left.

Possibly too grand for the Post Office?

→thing in the morning, it's unreasonable."
Unreasonable! I am never unreasonable! Is this the first chink in our marriage? How can I look our neighbours in the eye again?

The sun is shining, the birds sing and the apple blossom abounds in The Avenue, but still it is a dark day. Richard is in mid-life crisis! When I asked him which hat I should wear to go into town to talk to the Post Office about ensuring all our letters arrive with first-class stamps, he said, I hate decisions of this magnitude. First→

12 TUESDAY

I said to Richard, "You know, dear, in times of crisis—and we are surely facing a time of crisis now—I think it helps if people sing together."

Richard was not enthusiastic, but I sat myself at the piano (virtually a Bechstein, I believe) and began to play

"What shall we sing together?"

"There's A Hole In My Bucket", said Richard

13 WEDNESDAY I fear this is a major crisis.

Richard is counting the days to Easter so that he can put sugar on his cornflakes again.

14 THURSDAY

I've spent the day polishing. When I'm under pressure, I always find it very reassuring to polish something. Polishing's so therapeutic.

FRIDAY 15

Elizabeth came round for coffee as usual, and spilled it over my cushioned tile flooring as usual. It is good to know, even in times of great crisis, that we still carry out our obligations to those less socially skilled than ourselves.

SATURDAY 16

We were driving into town together this morning, when I made up my mind. "We shall fight it together, Richard," I said. "I shall be a tower of strength for you. Watch out for other women!"

"Where? Where?" said Richard, always the careful driver.

"In your mid-life crisis. It's a time when men think of other women."

"Not me Hyacinth. I assure you," said dear Richard. "for me one woman is enough."

A beautiful sentiment. I think he is getting better.

17 SUNDAY   MOTHERING SUNDAY

As usual, a lovely card from Sheridan, even though I had to buy it myself. I know the thought is there and I am sure he will ring me for a mother and child heart-to-heart as soon as he and his dear friend Tarquin get back from wherever it is they have gone. Sheridan's card had such a lovely message: "Mother dear, you are always there when troubles cloud the sky."
I showed it to Emmet and Elizabeth, and they said, "How true. You always seem to be there when troubles cloud our skies too".

Mother dear, you are always there
When troubles cloud the sky

18 MONDAY

Daisy tells me she had a rather gaudy card from her Stephanie, complete with rusk stains provided by her   little Kylie, which Daisy was thrilled with even though the sentiment was less romantic. "Mum. Love You. Lend us a tenner." Where do they get these things from?

TUESDAY 19

Richard has bought himself a new tweed jacket! It is identical to another one in his wardrobe, but it is the first item of clothing that Richard has ever bought unprompted.

WEDNESDAY 20

I cannot find Richard's other jacket, the one the same as the one he has just bought himself. Richard has not mentioned it, but then he never does talk about his clothing much. He has innate dress sense, which comes from being married to me.

THURSDAY 21

Richard has spent several hours today with Reggie Thorgunby, the man who managed the department which used to rely on Richard so much. The Council Crisis is surely still with us, although Richard will not talk about it.

22 FRIDAY

Ladies' Luncheon Club. Manor House Function Rooms, Moreton Road, 12.00.
Richard to manage on his own.
I think he did.
The crossword was filled in when I returned.

23 SATURDAY

Time for another Candle Light Supper. The Millburns, Mr and Mrs. Councillor Nugent, and perhaps Porky Hooton, the golfer, and his wife. Richard gets on so well with Porky. It will have to be after the end of Lent. I could not face the Frostide Millburns during a period when Richard is unable to sprinkle sugar on their star product.

The Ladies' Luncheon Club,
March Meeting.
Manor House Function Rooms,
Moreton Road, 12 noon.
Hats and gloves to be worn.

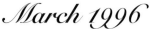

SUNDAY 24

The vicar's sermon was on the beauties of spring, all about the lilies of the field which toil not, neither do they spin. It made me realise how much we had neglected the garden this year, so I asked Richard to take me for a little 'spin' (a joke) to C.D. Benedict's garden centre. We bought all sorts of lovely things — an antique reproduction rustic garden bench in mock pine, a trellis for the back garden and some new shears as I fear there were some green marks on our other ones, which even hard polishing does not completely remove. Leaf or grass stains, I suppose, but I have asked Richard to be more careful with the new ones.

MONDAY 25

Richard spent several happy hours in the garden this afternoon, making sure that our garden, at least, is arrayed like Solomon in all his glory, as I think the vicar put it yesterday. I wore my pink silk scarf, to match the ~~apple blossom~~. peach blossom.

26 TUESDAY

It is Easter in ten days. I need to sort out my hats.

27 WEDNESDAY

I am in need of another hat. Or perhaps two. Richard thinks I have enough, but he just does not understand. Do you ever see Mrs. Wilkinson, that lady who is so pretentious she has even been burgled, in the same hat twice?

28 THURSDAY

Richard asked if I'd ever seen Violet's Bruce in the same hat twice. He is missing the point.

Richard says it would not be right to buy another hat during Lent, a time of restraint. He has a point, and at least I am glad that his moments of religious doubt seem to have lifted enough for him to point out the subtler points of dogma to me.

Marston Hall. I have decided it will add atmosphere if we place silver-framed photographs in suitable positions, so I have been sorting out photographs while Richard has been dispatched to the jewellers to buy enough silver photograph frames for our purposes. I do so love the one of dear Sheridan as a daffodil. He has such astonishing stage presence.

31 SUNDAY — BRITISH SUMMER TIME BEGINS

We have spent the day putting our photographs up around the living-room. Richard only
bought three silver frames, but we have the one
of Sheridan as a boy scout over the mantelpiece,
the one of Sheridan completing his one width
doggy paddle (for which he won a certificate,
which perhaps we ought to
frame for the master bedroom)
on the far wall, and in the
entrance hall the one of
Sheridan's most intricate
piece of needlework, a
rainbow of dazzling colours.
The place looks so much more
like home now.

1 MONDAY

Daisy rang to tell me that their house had fallen down.
I was not at all surprised, but she went on to say that as
they had nowhere else to live, they were going to move
into Marston Hall at once.

Even wearing my second-best blue dress, I could feel
the colour drain from my face. "Could'nt you go to Violet's?"
I asked. Then there was much laughing down the
telephone. "April Fool!" Will Daisy never grow up?

TUESDAY 2

I found a rose in Richard's jacket pocket as I was getting it ready for the dry cleaners. He said it was for me but he had forgotten to give it to me. How sweet of him! I wonder when he bought it.

WEDNESDAY 3

I found another rose in Richard's coat pocket when I was checking it for old handkerchiefs and other pieces of litter. He said that was for me as well but he had forgotten to give it to me. His memory is really getting bad. I must feed him more carrots. Or is it cauliflower that is good for the memory? I forget.

MAUNDY THURSDAY　　　　　　　**THURSDAY 4**

This is Maundy Thursday. Her Majesty looked splendid distributing the Maundy money to the old folk. She was wearing a hat just like one of mine.

5 FRIDAY

GOOD FRIDAY

Lent is almost over, so I can plan our next entertainment. It will be on a Thursday, a day of the week that always seems to need brightening up. A truly hospitable household bestows Candle Light Suppers on every day of the week.

6 SATURDAY

Richard says the rain makes it impossible for him to clean the car. I told him to clean the car inside the garage, where it is not raining, but he says it is too dark. Honestly, he does get so easily discouraged sometimes. A man with his electrical skills, strictly at the executive level, of course, but nevertheless well proven with our Christmas Tree lights, should be able to install lighting into the garage without a second thought. He says he would need to drive into town to buy the necessary electrical devices, but as he cannot be seen driving a dirty car, it will have to wait for another occasion. Richard is so thoughtful sometimes. It's just a pity that his thoughtfulness precludes any constructive action.

April 1996

Elizabeth is away for the holiday, staying with her daughter Gail who lives so openly with somebody called Harold, of all things. I cannot approve of such liaisons, especially on Easter Day, and said so to Emmet.

"A broken marriage is worse than no marriage at all", he said. That's a very odd thought. Is a broken Royal Doulton tea service worse than no Royal Doulton tea service at all? I don't think so. There are always bits you can salvage.

Emmet is so helpless on his own. I invited him in for coffee, but he was three minutes late and spilt his coffee over my newly relacquered herringbone. I told him I thought he was very deep, but he said no, he was a tenor usually, with just a few overtones of baritone when he has a cold.

9 TUESDAY

Emmet came in for coffee again. The Hawkesworth clumsiness was in full flow. He spilt his coffee all over my (unbroken) Royal Doulton plate of royally appointed bourbon biscuits, just as I was getting into the swing of my 'Highlights from Sir Andrew Lloyd Webber'. My singing can have an unsettling effect, I know. Even the deafest of the

10 WEDNESDAY old folk tell me that.

Emmet has had to go to join Elizabeth with her Gail. Some sudden crisis, he said.

11 THURSDAY Candle Light Supper 7.30
Green flowered dress with two rows of pearls.
~~The Frosticle Millburns~~ (New Product Launch! How exciting! How maritime!)
~~Porky and Mrs Porky Hooton~~ (Golf tournament in Tenerife)
~~Elizabeth and Emmet~~ (some sudden crisis)
~~Mr and Mrs. Councillor Nugent~~ (this Council Crisis is still with us)
The Major ~~and Mrs Wilton Smythe~~ (pyrophobia)
The vicar and his young wife
Another resounding success.

At C.P. Benedict's this morning, C.P. mentioned that he is exhibiting at the Chelsea Flower Show next month.

We shall be there.

Marston Hall. I bumped into Sir Edward in the corridor, and was able to have a few quiet words with him. I am sure he will accept my invitation to tea and cucumber sandwiches as soon as his gouty foot allows him to climb up the stairs to our little eyrie. What an elegant disability gout is! It suits him.

Invitation

....

are cordially invited to a

Candle Light Supper

....

R.S.V.P. THE RESIDENCE, BLOSSOM AVENUE

14 SUNDAY

Marston Hall. What a pleasant day! Richard and I enjoyed a little drive. The rain did not cause too many problems, even in the narrow lanes, and the Land Rover pulling the horse box had only itself to blame for swerving into the ditch and becoming entangled with a rather quaint stone wall. I was a little surprised that the driver did not comment on my hat, a bold statement in maroon and green, as he jumped out of his rather grubby vehicle and raced towards us through the mud, but he could see that we were not dressed to help him and his horse out of the ditch. This did not stop him from making some suggestions as to how we could best be of assistance, but I decline to record them in full in the pages of such a well-ordered diary.

15 MONDAY

"Drive on Richard", I said, and drive on we did.

It is time to consider our holiday. We do of course now own a modest foothold in the shires, at Marston Hall, but there is more to see than just the countryside. We must choose carefully.

LIMASSOL

HA

BALMYRA BEACH APARTMENTS

SP

Lo
on t
kilo
of
loc
style wings tucke
the spacious grounds.
Amenities are outdoor
swimming pool, sun terraces,

What an idylic location the Balmyra Beach Apartments has – situated directly on the beach. The Old Town and main shopping area of Limassol is 8 km away. For families and for those wl

TUESDAY 16

Delia Wheelwright, who lives in the mock Tudor two-storey semi at the corner of Oakdale Avenue, has let it be known that they intend to vacation in Bermuda this year. I do so disapprove of the word 'vacation'. It sounds so industrial.

WEDNESDAY 17

Richard went out looking a little worried. He came back some hours later looking a little happier. He has been at the golf club, apparently, with Porky Hooton and the Major. I hope he is taking his early retirement seriously.

THURSDAY 18

We have collected several brochures and national press advertisements. I have decided against the QEII again, as everybody knows we had such a wonderful time last time (although the local newspaper only mentioned the fact that Daisy and Onslow had won a free cruise. Our fully paid up outward-facing cabin tickets were not mentioned).

19 FRIDAY

Elizabeth and Emmet are back. Elizabeth says Gail and Harold are going to Tuscany. Tuscany! That sounds not too foreign, but still rather elegant. I wonder where it is.

20 SATURDAY

It's in Italy. Not far from Rome, according to the Major, who we met in the High Street this morning. I think that would suit us very well. "Even the Ranks of Tuscany could scarce forbear to cheer," was what the Major said when I mentioned we may be holidaying there this year. Who are the Ranks of Tuscany? Are they related to the Ranks who own the bakery?

April 1996

An interesting sermon. Joseph and his Coat Of Many Colours and something about pride in the way one looks. The vicar seems to think that pride is a sin. I've always thought he was a little too young and radical for our church, and will mention it to the bishop next time I see him. Such a nice man, the bishop, and he takes pride in his purple robes and his gaiters, I'm sure.

SMART HOLIDAYS
(prop. W.B. and D.D. Smart)
Two Week Tuscan Holiday Adventure

The perfect holiday for less than £3000

TOP TUSCAN TOURS FOR THE DISCERNING HOLIDAY MAKER
The best hotels!
The most delicious food!
The brightest sunshine!
And all for less than the price of a Rolls Royce!

I have been unable to find out whether the Ranks of Tuscany are worth knowing. And are there too many Italians there? Ought we to book up for a Two week Tuscan Holiday Adventure or do we feel that if everybody else is going to Tuscany, the Buckets ought to be somewhere else? Richard must decide.

23 TUESDAY

The birthday of Her Majesty the Queen. I wore my red shoes, white handbag and blue flower dress in celebration of the occasion. Richard had a haircut, which is a patriotic gesture, I suppose.

24 WEDNESDAY

Richard says Tuscany is fine. When I suggested the castles of the Loire Valley (fewer Italians), he said fine. When I said that maybe Vienna and a little opera would be the perfect way to relax away from The Avenue, he said fine. He seems distracted.

25 THURSDAY

I think we can just about afford this off season.

Wales

Mid-Wales
17th C former stables, twixt coast and country. Slps 3, wild garden. Avail mid-May to end Oct.
(01252) 613183

FRIDAY 26

Reggie and Fiona Thorgunby are going sailing in Turkey. Well, not in Turkey so much as next to it, in the Mediterranean. Richard is of maritime stock, and he already has a sailor's outfit from that day on the river a few years back. Maybe we should listen to the call of the sea for our summer's recreation.

SATURDAY 27

Marston Hall. The daffodils are blooming to match my new yellow spring hat. Richard and I sat in the sunshine looking at brochures for expensive holidays. The food in Tuscany is supposed to be wonderful. I think I shall try out a few traditional recipes of the region and have a summer Tuscan Temptation Alfresco for a few of our dearest friends. That may be more effective than actually going there. Richard does not like the sun very much.

28 SUNDAY

Sir Edward was impressed by the weight of our holiday research materials. He seems rather a crybaby for somebody who has won the MC and bar. I cannot believe a few brochures falling on a gouty foot can hurt more than foreign bullets. What a fuss he made!

So we have driven home a little early, which caused a reaction with Emmet and Elizabeth as they saw our car arrive back in The Avenue shortly after lunch. It is so wonderful to have neighbours who think so much of us.

29 MONDAY

I have bought an interesting book called 'Tastes of Tuscany'. I must begin trying out some of the recipes on Richard.

TUESDAY 30

Richard does not like Pappardelle al Sugo di Arrosto. It needs Italian wholemeal bread. I think the Ranks of Tuscany must be the people who own the bakery.

Giving Sir Edward a little guidance.

WEDNESDAY 1

Richard does not like Insalata di Fagioli Borlotti, so that's no good for my Tuscan Temptation Alfresco.

THURSDAY 2

I can't offer my guests something called Acqua Cotta. That means 'Cooked Water', although the ingredients seem to include mushrooms and tomatoes as well, which shows how imprecise the Italians can be.

3   FRIDAY

Sheridan telephoned! He is back in England in time for the term. Apparently he has joined a club at his place of learning called the Worker's Revolutionary Committee. It is wonderful that he is being chosen to sit on committees, but it is a pity that a Bucket could not find an Executive's Revolutionary Committee, which is far more appropriate for somebody of our social heritage.

4   SATURDAY

Richard does not understand the links that bond mother and child. He says that if Sheridan is a Worker, he does not need the £500 he asked for. "If he wants to be really revolutionary, he could stop asking me for money." I said he needs it for his youthful activities, but Richard just suggested he should be a little less active. But this is a boy who gained swimming certificates before he was into his teens! He is active by pedigree.

SUNDAY 5

Marston Hall. Richard does not like the idea of Rabbit St. Angelo or Pigeon in Olives. The Tuscanians eat some strange things.

Richard's eyes and boots both sparkle.

MAY DAY BANK HOLIDAY   MONDAY 6

Marston Hall. I really do not think it's appropriate to celebrate a May Day holiday, designed as it is for the Worker. Richard and I managed to avoid being caught up in any political marches, however.

May 1996

7 TUESDAY

Sheridan telephoned again! He said he was only allowed one call, but I said he could phone as often as he liked. He asked to speak to his father. The conversation then revolved around £50, which Richard described as 'fine', so maybe he is feeling more paternal towards our only son.

8 WEDNESDAY

Richard has explained that Sheridan helped to organise a brisk springtime Workers March for Freedom on Monday! Thanks to a misunderstanding over the route of the walk, which went past the council offices just as some sort of protest was going on, Sheridan was taken to the police station for his own safety. Once the situation had been explained to the magistrate, Richard was able to take Sheridan back to college.

9 THURSDAY

Richard says that it was just that Sheridan needed to celebrate the May Day Bank Holiday in the way that students and workers have done for many years. The magistrate understood that. What's wrong with Whitsun, I want to know? I must call the vicar for clarification of that point.

FRIDAY 10

Perhaps Sheridan should give up all these rough physical exercises and stick to his embroidery, at least until he is old enough to play executive golf. I will ask Richard to lend him his clubs, so that he can practise hitting.

SATURDAY 11

Rose's birthday tomorrow. What do you give a woman who has been given all that life has to offer, several times? We decided on an address book and organiser, which I feel will help her to keep track of her social life. Richard says that Rose would rather not keep too much track of her social life, but that must be wrong. Everybody wants to remember every detail of those people with whom they have had social dealings, don't they?

12 SUNDAY

Rose liked our present. Their house looked as usual like something from the Bosnian front line from the outside, but inside it was a blaze of flowers. Boris sent two dozen roses. So did Mr. Bartholomew. There were further floral tributes from Mr. Bickerstaff, Mr. Crabtree, Mr. Finchley, Mr. Murchison and Reg. Mr. Marinopoulos gave her a gold and diamond brooch, and Daisy and Onslow gave her a dishcloth and apron. Daddy gave her a kiss, which would have been fine if he had not already blacked himself up with Onslow's boot polish, ready to go out on a sortie with Colonel Dawlish. Dark tan is surprisingly hard to remove from a daughter's cheek.

13 MONDAY

The tickets for our visit to the Chelsea Flower Show have arrived! I shall wear my brightest red outfit, to make a statement about the beauty of the English country garden.

TUESDAY 14

We have set the date for our Tuscan Temptation Alfresco. It will be on Saturday 25th at Marston Hall, so that we can hold it in those wonderful gardens, with all the ~~roadident~~ ~~rhododandetions~~ hollyhocks in bloom, or whatever blooms in late May.

WEDNESDAY 15

Charity Shop Day. Violet's Bruce came in while Mrs. Councillor Nugent was explaining the importance of suppressing excessive romantic behaviour. He immediately began looking along the rack of ladies' evening wear, and despite my subtle guidings towards the men's suits, he would not be diverted. He selected a simple off the shoulder black dress which would have suited Violet well (if she needed to shop in charity shops, of course). Bruce then asked where the

THURSDAY 16

fitting room was, and did we have any black lace negligees. I decided against introducing him to Mrs Councillor Nugent, even though he has room for a pony. He left without buying anything.

Richard says that Mr. Councillor Nugent often remarks on the fact that Mrs. Councillor Nugent is an expert on the suppression of excessive romantic behaviour.

17 FRIDAY

Why was Richard talking to Mr. Councillor Nugent? He has been out of the house a great deal recently. The Council Crisis continues, perhaps.

18 SATURDAY

> *Invitation*
>
> ## Mr and Mrs Councillor Nugent
>
> *are cordially invited to a*
>
> *Tuscan Temptation Alfresco*
> **25th May at Marston Hall**
> **7.30 for 8 pm. Dress informal**
>
> R.S.V.P. THE RESIDENCE, BLOSSOM AVENUE

Marston Hall. Tuscan Temptation Alfresco,
     next weekend's guest list:
~~Reggie & Fiona Thorgunby~~ (Busy. Silly squeaky voice she has anywa.
Mr. & Mrs. Councillor Nugent
~~Porky & Mrs. Porky Hooton~~ (Golf tournament in Florida)
Elizabeth & Emmet
The Major and ~~Mrs Wilton-Smythe~~ (agoraphobia)
The vicar and his young wife (to discuss the importance
                                                    of Whitsun)

SUNDAY 19

Marston Hall. The Thorgunbys cannot come so we rang the Frosticle Millburns. He is opening a new factory that day. I did not realise you made Frosticles in factories! We shall revert to the Dutch royal family's favourite breakfast cereal, which does not, I am sure, involve the industrial process. Bunty and Dorian? And of course Sir Edward.

MONDAY 20

Daisy rang. Can we have Daddy next weekend? Rose, Daisy and Onslow have been invited to a party on Saturday, and don't want to leave Daddy. How can I have him? Can I disguise him as a Tuscan waiter? It will never work.

21 TUESDAY   *Chelsea Flower Show*

Richard says he will look after Daddy. I have decided that the certain absence of Daisy, Rose and Onslow from my Tuscan Temptation Alfresco outweighs the slight possibility of Daddy misunderstanding the social significance of the occasion. It will be a great success.

---

22 WEDNESDAY   *Chelsea Flower Show*

Tomorrow is our day at the Chelsea Flower Show. It will be marvellous. Richard has booked our train tickets, first class of course, and a taxi will take us to the show itself. I expect royalty will be there, although of course I will not thrust myself forward.

And Bunty and Dorian have said yes! Richard has bought 6 more bottles of whisky.

23 THURSDAY   *Chelsea*

CHELSEA
FLOWER
SHOW

ADMIT
1

To the Chelsea Flower Show. C.P's display was quite marvellous. I wore my best red suit and royalty was there! The Crown Prince of Uzbekistan, I believe. A nice man who spoke very little English, but enjoyed my showing him the photo of Sheridan as a daffodil. I invited him to our Tuscan Temptation Alfresco on Saturday, but he cannot come. A state funeral I think he said. I am sure that won't be as much fun as our function.

Chelsea Flower Show

To Marston Hall to prepare for the big day. I have brought several different outfits, as we do not know if the weather will hold. Richard has bought a book on Tuscany, but I prefer to rely on instinct and the regional feelings that cooking their rather strange foods will bring. Tuscany is apparently the place where they eat game, but that's a bit chewy for Daddy so I have decided on ravioli, which is Italian enough for most of them.

Tuscan Temptation Alfresco, a lunchtime Italian experience for my dearest friends. Ravioli and parmesan cheese, followed by Italian ice cream.

Another great success. Mr. and Mrs. Councillor Nugent rang early on to say they could not come as Mr. Councillor Nugent had suddenly developed the flu, but everybody else was there. The vicar and his wife have apparently spent many happy holidays in Tuscany, so they were able to talk with Richard about that, while it turned out that Daddy and Sir Edward had both served with Col. Dawlish in our Time of Greatest Crisis. I believe Daddy's war record is superior to Sir Edward's, but at least they were able to talk happily about old times, at least until Daddy shot Sir Edward in the foot with his army rifle.

Bunty and Dorian brought Daisy, Onslow and Rose along. I'd forgotten they knew each other. At least it didn't rain.

26 SUNDAY

A little clearing up to be done after our Tuscan Temptation Alfresco. Daddy's stray bullet which shot Sir Edward was just a flesh wound, really, as it passed through his bandages and embedded itself in the front door of Marston Hall. Richard has almost repaired the woodwork. It looks so much better now.

I do try not to notice the spills.

27 MON BANK HOLIDAY

By the way, it turns out that neither Bunty nor Sir Edward, nor indeed Mrs. Councillor Nugent have met the Crown Prince of Uzbekistan. I will introduce them one day.

TUESDAY 28

I spoke to the vicar about Whitsun, but he seemed to think it was still on the Christian calendar. It's only the list of Bank Holidays it has been removed from, apparently. Richard says it doesn't really matter, because we don't work anyway. Don't work! What does he think my Tuscan Temptation Alfresco was? That was work, just as the Crown Prince of Uzbeckhistan's state funeral was work.

WEDNESDAY 29

A beautiful day. But Richard's gone out again. We don't seem to do as much together as we used to do.

THURSDAY 30

Elisabeth in for coffee. She spilled Kenyan Dark Ground all over my new 'Views of Windsor' coasters, but I tried not to notice.

31 FRIDAY

Richard and I visited Sir Edward in hospital. He looked quite fit to me, but he said he did not think he would be back at Marston Hall for some time, poor man.

1 SATURDAY

I wanted to go back to Marston Hall this weekend, and thought it would be fine with Sir Edward not yet out of hospital. But Richard suggested a weekend in The Avenue, so we relaxed at home. A wonderful sunny day, and Richard spent several hours in the garden, pruning the roses. I found another one in his pocket later.

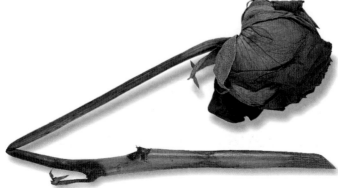

Daisy rang. Apparently it is Derby Day next weekend and Dorian, who knows somebody at the Jockey Club, has invited Onslow and Daisy to go to the Derby, which this year is being held in Epsom. Daisy wants to borrow one of my hats.

Richard must know somebody in the Jockey Club. Reggie Thorgunby is rather a small man. I expect he was a jockey once.

Reggie Thorgunby is not a member of the Jockey Club. Nor is C.P. Benedict or The Douglas Chater. What is the point of achieving a respected place in society if you cannot use your influence to allow close friends access to the best occasions?

4 TUESDAY

Bruce and Violet have room for a pony, but they know nobody at the Jockey Club.

5 WEDNESDAY

I telephoned Bunty to suggest it would be lovely if we could all travel to Epsom as a sixsome, but she said that there was not room for six in their car. It's a Rolls-Royce apparently, but with a chauffeur and picnic equipment, they can only take four passengers. Although I am sure they would rather be seen with Richard and I than with Daisy and Onslow, they cannot go back on an invitation once given.

6 THURSDAY

Noblesse oblige.

I cannot worry about the Derby. I am sure that horse racing is all very well, but it is not cultural. The Royal Academy Summer Exhibition, on the other hand, has just opened and that is very cultural. Richard and I plan to visit it very soon.

Daisy came round to borrow a hat. I suggested at the same time that Richard lend Onslow a shirt, but Daisy said he did not need one. She chose my wide brimmed purple hat complete with bunch of grapes. I hope nobody recognises it.

Epsom Derby

Marston Hall. What a pleasant day! Richard and I relaxed, enjoying the rural grandeur of our piece of Britain. There was nothing else going on anywhere in the world, as far as we could tell, and we were able to spend a day without worrying about our place on the social ladder. We did not even turn on the television, as there was nothing much on except for some horse racing, which I regret to say does not interest me.

for six months.

ROYAL ACADEMY
Summer Exhibition

MONDAY-FRIDAY 9AM TO 8PM

SATURDAY AND SUNDAY 9.30AM TO 9PM

THE CULTURAL EVENT OF THE YEAR

9 SUNDAY

On our return to The Avenue, we were greeted cheerily by Emmet, who told us how much fun it was to see Onslow and Daisy on the television from Epsom, even if Daisy was wearing a perfectly dreadful hat. Apparently they were interviewed by somebody looking for 'local colour'. As long as everybody thinks they are local to Epsom rather than to me, I shall be all right.

10 MONDAY

Bumped into the Major this morning. He too commented on Daisy and Onslow's starring role in the television broadcast, but said it was a pity Daisy was wearing such an unsuitable hat. "Ascot's the place for hats," he said, "Not Epsom."

TUESDAY 11

The television broadcast was on *Channel Four*! How could any member of my family agree to be seen alongside the naked bodies and alternative comedians of that regrettable channel? Why couldn't they have been interviewed by that nice BBC man with the ears?

WEDNESDAY 12

Daisy brought back the hat she borrowed. "Keep it," I said. "It suits you better than it does me."

THURSDAY 13

I have discovered that Royal Ascot, where hats are worn, begins next week. What is more, there is a Ladies' Day next Thursday. Richard and I will be there.

June 1996

14 FRIDAY

Richard seems to think it may be difficult to get tickets for the Royal Enclosure at Ascot. He seems very reluctant to hire a morning suit, even to accompany me in my new hat! I have bought a stunning broad-brimmed white silk hat trimmed with roses, leeks and thistles and something unrecognisable which could be clover, if that is the national flower of Ireland.

15 SATURDAY

A quiet day. We watched the Trooping The Colour on television and Richard cut several roses in

SUPERIOR HATS

1 Ascot Delight
multi-flower
white silk with roses,
leeks and thistles

£112-

honour of the occasion. Her Majesty was not wearing an outfit which would clash with mine next Thursday, but she looked very nice all the same.

Marston Hall. Dorian and Bunty are not going to Royal Ascot, but they do not appear to have any tickets they could let us have. I am telephoning all those who might be interested in Royal Ascot, to let them know that we are going and could join their party if they are one couple short.

Even on the golf course it is vital to dress for the occasion.

The Douglas Chater would love to join us at Royal Ascot, but he has to put business first, he says. Sir Edward is still fussing over that slight flesh wound Daddy gave him, and is not available to be approached. I cannot find the telephone number of the Crown Prince of Uzzbekastan.

18 TUESDAY

Ascot

Delia Wheelwright will not be joining us at Royal Ascot, and neither will Porky Hooton, who does not like horses despite his public school background. I have hired a morning suit for Richard, and a top hat to make him look as distinguished as a man of his social calibre needs to look. He may even be mistaken for a minor Royal if he remembers to take the lens cap off his binoculars.

19 WEDNESDAY

Ascot

All we need now is an invitation to the Royal Enclosure. With Richard's morning suit and my broad-brimmed white silk hat trimmed with roses, leeks and thistles, it should be a mere formality. I am so excited.

20 THURSDAY ~~Royal Ascot Ladies Day~~ Ascot

What a pleasant day we had at the Royal Academy Summer Exhibition! We had never intended to do anything else, despite finding ourselves briefly at the Ascot Racecourse, where a rather coarse steward refused us admission to the Royal Enclosure. I expect he thought we would show up the other guests, who were far less strikingly dressed than us. We certainly made an impression at the Royal Academy.

Ascot   FRIDAY 21

Richard is complaining about the painting we
bought at the R.A. But what is money when acquiring
an original work of art? It's a glorious explosion of
colour entitled 'Woman: Prone', by a certain Reg Higginbottom, which I am almost certain is a nom de plume
(or de paintbrush) of the Prince Of Wales, and it will
be delivered to The Avenue in due course in a very small
van bearing the Royal Academy's coat of arms.

SATURDAY 22

Marston Hall. Richard is being most
difficult. Modern art is not meant to be beautiful.
It is not meant to be understood. It is meant
to be a talking point. It is meant to be expensive.
Richard says that at almost £2,000 it will
certainly be a talking point, mainly with
the bank manager.

23 SUNDAY

Marston Hall. Delia Wheelwright does not own an original Reg Higginbottom. Nor does Mrs. Drummond from the Grange, nor Bunty and Dorian, who make do with paintings of swooning Romans by somebody called Alma Tadema. She was a singer, I remember, and rather better at singing than painting, if I am any judge. The Major said he would like to come and cast his eye over my Higginbottom any time, so I may invite him to our next entertainment.

24 MONDAY   Wimbledon starts

Richard rushed off this morning straight after breakfast. He came back several hours later, looking a little dishevelled, but it seems he had run into Onslow in the town and they had spent an hour in the pub. Onslow is a bad influence, and I must tell him so.

TUESDAY 25

Onslow says he did not see Richard yesterday, although he readily admits he spent more than an hour in the pub. He must have consumed so much beer his memory is beginning to be affected. That proves what a bad influence on Richard he is.

WEDNESDAY 26

The weather is set fair for the weekend, so we will entertain our friends with my special Outdoors Indoors Luxury Barbecue. Richard says if the weather is set fair, why can't we have an Outdoors Outdoors Luxury Barbecue, but he misses the point. Anybody can do Outdoors Outdoors. It takes a Bucket to think of Outdoors Indoors.

THURSDAY 27

Outdoors Indoors Luxury Barbecue, guest list:

~~Reggie + Fiona Thorgunby~~ (Busy. If I understand her silly squeaky voice)

~~Mr + Mrs. Frosticles Millburn~~ (Royal Warrant Holders Annual Barndance)

~~Porky + Mrs Porky Hooton~~ (Golf Tournament in Adelaide)

Elizabeth and Emmet

The Major and ~~Mrs. Wilton-Smythe~~ (arachnophobia)

C.P. Benedict and partner

The vicar and his young wife (to discuss the importance of modern art)

28 FRIDAY

To C.P. Benedict's Garden Centre to buy all the foliage for our Outdoors Indoors Luxury Barbecue. I will wear a rustic milk-maid's outfit and the entire evening will be green and charming.

29 SATURDAY

Our Outdoors Indoors Luxury Barbecue. All in all, another great success. C.P. Benedict's partner turned out to be Rose, which was nice. She was wearing enough to cover her basics, at least. Despite the weather forecast, there were a few spots of rain, which meant that Richard got a little wet barbecuing the steaks, but Emmet was very good in staying outside to keep him company, however much I tried to persuade him to come inside and entertain the guests with selections from 'Oklahoma' while the barbecue got going. The vicar's wife drank three glasses of sweet sherry, and Elizabeth dropped most of her mixed grill onto a Mexican fern behind which the Major had positioned himself.

SUNDAY 30

To church. Richard sneezed throughout the service. The vicar preached about Mary and Martha, the sisters who were so different, yet Jesus loved them both. Few of us combine the qualities of the two sisters in one person. I keep my house in perfect condition, just like Martha, but still find time to join in the conversation when entertaining at home, just like Mary.

1 bottle sweet sherry
(to replace amount consumed by vicar's dear young wife)

1 jar Royal Appointment Orange marmalade

Greenfly spray

1 packet non-prescription hay fever pills

MONDAY 1

Richard has hay fever. He says it is a cold from trying to light a barbecue in the rain, but I know it is hay fever. He is not good company.

2 TUESDAY

Delia Wheelwright and I were discussing the Royal Academy Summer Show, which she has not visited, when she mentioned that Miss Winthorpe has an invitation to a Royal Garden Party next week! Little Miss Winthorpe, who is even frightened of Daddy, is going to Buckingham Palace!

3 WEDNESDAY   Henley Royal Regatta

Apparently it is because Miss Winthorpe is Secretary of the Over 70s Club, so she 'qualifies' for an invitation! Well, in that case Richard and I 'qualify' too. Richard is highly thought of in charitable circles and Sheridan has been rebuilding Romania. And Daddy frequently takes the very clothes off his back for good causes. Our invitation must have got lost in the post.

4 THURSDAY

Michael, our postman, would, I am sure, welcome a day with fewer letters to carry to our house. Normally we are inundated with correspondence, all first class of course, which Michael delivers to the best of his ability despite his twitch. The well being of our postman must not take precedence over the successful delivery of Her Majesty's mail.

FRIDAY 5

I have telephoned the Palace to find out what has happened to our invitation. I was wearing my red, white and blue scarf and drinking a cup of tea from my Coronation Mug, but this seemed to make no difference to the man's attitude. He had no record of anybody of our name, even though I spelt it quite clearly for him. He obviously has the wrong list, or else has not sufficient security clearance to see the full list.

SATURDAY 6

Miss Winthorpe is flouting her Garden Party invitation by refusing to buy a new dress. I offered to lend her a hat, as so many people have heard that my hat wardrobe is second to none, but she was not interested. "Your head is rather bigger than mine," she said, and it is true that her rather unenterprising hairdo would not fill any hat as elegantly as mine does.

7 SUNDAY   Wimbledon Finals Day

   I invited Emmet and Elizabeth for
Darjeeling tea and cucumber sandwiches, with
a hint of cress, but they said it was Wimbledon
Finals day and they would be watching television.
To watch television on such a glorious afternoon
seems a great pity, especially when all you are
looking at is some shabbily dressed young Americans
hitting a ball at each other.
   Richard spent several hours in the
garden instead.

8 MONDAY

   Our invitation to the Royal Garden Party
has definitely gone astray. I have telephoned
the Post Office, who said they would look into
it. I told them it required more than a bit
of looking. It requires action. At that point
we were cut off.

TUESDAY 9

I tried once again to contact somebody with some authority at the Palace, having first polished the pearl-handled slimline touchtone telephone, of course. But we were cut off.

WEDNESDAY 10

Could they have mistaken Winthorpe for Bucket? It's an easy enough mistake to make. I'm sure that man at the Palace has illegible handwriting. He sounded like the sort of man who does not dot his i's or cross his t's.

Royal Garden Party

THURSDAY 11

The day of Miss Winthorpe's Royal Garden Party. I do hope it all goes well for her, poor dear. The journey to London can be a trial for anybody who has to put up with the hurly-burly of public transport.

12 FRIDAY

Miss Winthorpe is back from the Royal Garden Party. She said it was wonderful. I am so pleased for her. Mrs Councillor Nugent drove her to London in her car. How sweet.

13 SATURDAY

Elizabeth came in for coffee. She spilt it, of course, this time over my new original mock-beech spice rack with oregano and thyme. She also mentioned that Emmet had once been to a Royal Garden Party, something to do with his music. He said it was an awful scrum. Hundreds of people in uncomfortable hired suits rummaging around looking for a spare sandwich and praying it would not rain. And Her Majesty is only ever viewed from a distance.

I never actually wanted to go to the Garden Party, but it was the principle of the thing. Invitations must be sent to those who deserve them, whether it is for social, charitable or musical reasons. I will write to the Palace and tell them.

On Thursday it will be Daisy's birthday. Unfortunately we do not have time to visit her then, so Richard drove me there today. We have given her a book token, as anything more practical would be wasted on her, I fear. How can a house look like hers fifty years after the Blitz?

Daddy was asleep. Richard looked relieved. He and Onslow went for a walk, which was a pity because I do hate to see Richard in the company of large sleeveless people. Could he not walk a pace or two behind, to give the impression they are not really brothers-in-law?

Here's a strange thing. Richard went out this morning wearing grey socks to match his trousers, and came back three hours later wearing dark navy socks to match his jacket. What could have caused his socks to change colour during a shopping expedition?

16 TUESDAY

I telephoned the vicar, to see what the church feels about Royal Garden Party invitations, but all he did was cough and splutter a great deal down my pearl-handled slimline touch-tone telephone, and then we were cut off. I think I need to talk to the telephone engineer.

17 WEDNESDAY

Telephone engineer 10.30a.m. 4.45pm. The telephone engineer has not arrived. How am I going to ensure against crossed lines from unexpected sources if the engineer does not arrive when he is summoned?

18 THURSDAY

Daisy's birthday. I rang to wish her a Happy Birthday but Rose said that she and Onslow could not be disturbed. She was reading her new book and Onslow was attuning his mind to the day's philosophical challenges. In other words, he was asleep.

FRIDAY 19

The telephone is still not working. I was in the middle of a call to British Telecom, as they now seem to call themselves, when it happened again. I was cut off in mid-sentence. It just is not good enough, and I would say so if only they could keep me connected for long enough.

SATURDAY 20

Marston Hall. I feel in need of a few days in retreat from the social demands of life in The Avenue. We shall spend the time in our rural wilderness just recharging our batteries and enjoying one another's company.

21 SUNDAY

I'm not sure that I am enjoying Richard's company at the moment. He seems to be very elusive even in our compact kitchenette where elusiveness is not an easy quality to display. For instance, he dried one of our Mary Rose glasses (the ones we bought in Portsmouth) several times over before he realised what he had done. His body is here, but his mind is elsewhere. He is obviously very distracted by something, but won't tell me what.

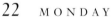

22 MONDAY

Richard says he is not worried about anything. I so want this place to be a haven of relaxation, but Richard will make no effort to relax. He looks the country squire when I get him properly dressed, but does not slip into the role that his clothes suggest. He has no interest in hunting, shooting and fishing, so I must make him interested.

Back from Marston Hall, Richard said if he wanted to go shooting, he'd rather do it at home. There was a little note in the door when we got back saying 'Telephone engineer called while you were out.' Honestly! What is the use of calling while you are out? Don't they know we have a rustic retreat with an exclusive postcode?

We called while you were out.

Please call 01252 234431 to make a new appointment.

Cowes Week begins soon. Sailing is in every Englishman's blood, whatever Richard may say, and I think it is our duty to go to Cowes for the fashionable part of the regatta. Prince Philip will probably be there and I can explain the mix-up over the garden party

It is decided. We set off for Cowes on Saturday, and we will stay on the island. We have decided not to spend the week taking part in the races, but we will cheer from the grandstand.

26   FRIDAY   Telephone engineer ~~10.30 a.m~~ 4.45 p.m.

The telephone engineer eventually arrived, and although I persuaded him to remove his shoes, he still managed to brush against the delicately patterned wallpaper in the hall. He said there was nothing wrong with the telephone, which of course is true. It is a pearl-handled slimline touchtone telephone with all the latest redial facilities. It is the <u>line</u> I am worried about. That ~~meanders carelessly under the roadways, passing so~~

27   SATURDAY   many houses about which one knows absolutely nothing.

To Cowes. Emmet and Elizabeth were naturally sorry to see us go, but they realise that our lives extend beyond The Avenue sometimes. They both remarked on my sailing outfit, a jaunty navy blue and white striped blouse with navy jacket, white cotton skirt and a white midshipman's bag. Richard refused to drive in his white sailing shorts, but otherwise looked delightfully nautical.

ISLE of WIGHT

Adult Day Ret

£7.40

T I M
FROM

Valid on 27/07/96

HO---ER TRAVEL

SUNDAY 28

The journey was rather longer than we expected. The road to Portsmouth goes through several villages twice and through Andover (an uninteresting town) four times. It was a beautifully sunny day, but Richard's mood did not always match the weather. We arrived in Portsmouth just too late for the last scheduled ferry, and they refused to put on another one for us, even though we had already bought our tickets in advance. So we had to spend the night in Portsmouth, in the only hotel which still had a room. It was not pleasant, but today we have arrived in Bembridge, and we have put yesterday's memories behind us. All the gaiety and excitement of Cowes Week lies ahead!

MONDAY 29

It has been raining. It is cold. Richard wonders why he did not bring his favourite jumper. He has not worn his shorts. The yachts all seem a long way away.

30 TUESDAY

Still raining. Still cold. We bumped into that round-the-world Commodore who spoke at the Women's Luncheon Club once. We will not bump into him again.

31 WEDNESDAY

No sign of Prince Philip. A few fireworks in the evenings, but Richard thinks this week is a damp squib. He is still not relaxing properly.

Hearts of Oak are our ships

1 THURSDAY

"Hearts of oak are our ships, hearts of oak are our men," is what I keep telling Richard, but I am not sure he believes it.

The cream of society is clearly not here. Not even the Crown Prince of ~~Uzbeckastan Uzbeckistin~~ Uzbekistan. So despite the fact that we have enjoyed ourselves thoroughly and the sea is in our blood, we will with a heavy heart make our way back to The Avenue tomorrow.

The journey home was much easier than the journey down. This time we caught the ferry without incident, although there was not time to go up on the bridge and discuss naval affairs with the Captain. Once we were back on dry land, we set off for home and this time only went through Andover once. As we were travelling along the motorway at a sensible speed, Richard wound down his window and unfortunately the wind caught his sailor's cap which I had asked him to wear for the ferry crossing. It flew away and is now somewhere in North Hampshire. I will have to buy another in time for next year.

4   SUNDAY

Daisy telephoned. Onslow has apparently won £10 on something called the National Lottery. Although I am naturally pleased that my sister's circumstances have improved by the sum of ten pounds, it is shaming to have to admit to a 'betterment of the family through the medium of gambling.

Richard's sailor's cap is now somewhere in North Hampshire.

5   MONDAY

Violet telephoned to say that she and Bruce have won £64 on the National Lottery. Despite already having room for a pony, my own sister is gambling with her lifestyle. That's what comes of marrying a turf accountant, especially one who always seems to need new clothes.

TUESDAY 6

Mrs. Fortescue, whose sister married a baronet but nevertheless does not have connections to attend Cowes Week, tells me that she regularly buys a Lottery ticket. Much of the proceeds go to charitable causes, so it clearly is an act of social responsibility to participate in the National Lottery.

WEDNESDAY 7

I have collected a Lottery card. Richard has collected a Lottery card. I have collected a Lottery card for Sheridan, and I have collected Lottery cards for both Elizabeth and Emmet. Nothing is too much trouble for a good cause.

THURSDAY 8

It appears that we have to choose six numbers, and if they match the numbers drawn, then we win a very large sum of money. The skill involved is in deciding which six numbers to choose.

9 FRIDAY

The first number will be 1, which is the number of widths doggy paddle that Sheridan swam. Then I will choose 8, which is the number of people who sit at our French polished extendible dining table for each Candle Light Supper. 12 is the number of Royal Doulton cups and saucers I inherited from Mummy, which makes 24 pieces of crockery. 34 is the number of hats in my wardrobe and 39 is Richards waist measurement.

10 SATURDAY

Richard was sent out to buy our lottery tickets, which he managed to do without too much delay. But we did not win. Perhaps I should have used my ebony refillable cartridge pen rather than Richard's ball point to fill out the form. I will not make the same mistake next week.

At least the charitable coffers of the nation are £3 richer tonight thanks to the generosity of the Buckets.

I don't think the vicar is fully aware of the meaning of the Lottery. I tried to explain to him at coffee after the service (sermon: how are the mighty fallen) that the money we all freely contribute goes to good causes like hospitals and the Chelsea Flower Show, but he prefers people to put an extra pound into the collection on Sunday. He said that then nobody loses.

We have heard from the Royal Academy in an embossed envelope. It seems that the Summer Exhibition has ended, so they can arrange for the Higginbottom that we bought to be delivered. How exciting.

13 TUESDAY

Richard is less excited because he says he will now have to pay for it. He said he had never paid for a 'Woman: Prone' in his life, and it seemed a pity to start now. I think he might have been attempting a rather vulgar joke.

14 WEDNESDAY

Richard spent much of the day with the bank manager. I have spent the day organising the delivery of our work of art. It will be delivered next Tuesday. The arrangements are almost complete.

15 THURSDAY

We will have an Art Appreciation Evening with Finger Buffet to unveil our Higginbottom. Saturday 24th.

FRIDAY 16

Guests:
~~Reggie + Fiona Thorgunby~~ (Busy. Clearly knows nothing about art)
~~Mr + Mrs. Frosticles Millburn~~ (Frosticles Annual General Meeting in Tuscany)
~~Porky + Mrs. Porky Hooton~~ (Golf tournament in Chepstow)
Elizabeth and Emmet
The Major and ~~Mrs. Wilton-Smythe~~ (xenophobia)
The Douglas Chater and partner.
The Vicar and his young wife (to discuss charitable concerns).

SATURDAY 17

1, 8, 12, 24, 34, 39. No luck again. Still, it is the principle that counts. Richard bought three tickets, saying that with any luck it would help him cover the cost of my Higginbottom. And he hasn't even seen it yet.

Dear Richard

18 SUNDAY

Just after a breakfast, the telephone rang. Richard answered it and a moment or two later announced he had to go out. He was not back until after our light Sunday luncheon vichyssoise had congealed and the salad had gone limp. A sudden Council Crisis, he said, but I begin to wonder. The council is so slow moving, I cannot believe it could summon up the energy to have a sudden crisis on a Sunday. Things are not all they seem.

19 MONDAY

Tomorrow is an important day in the cultural life of The Avenue. I think I have mentioned it, just in passing, to most of the people I know. Especially that Barker-Finch woman at number 23.

TUESDAY 20

The Royal Academy delivered our Higginbottom. They could have made a better job of it, I think. They turned up in an old van without any Royal markings on the side, pulled the painting out of the back, wrapped in an old blanket, and smuggled it to the back door as though they did not want anybody to see

"Can't be too careful with a valuable thing like this," they said. And then they were gone within two minutes.

WEDNESDAY 21

Richard is hanging our Higginbottom. It is difficult to decide exactly where it fits best. The overwhelming colours are yellow, maroon and black, which makes one wonder what sort of a woman (prone) he was painting. We have decided not to move the portrait of Sir Winston Churchill.

THURSDAY 22

Still a couple short for our Art Appreciation Evening. I'd invite my sister Violet and her Bruce if I didn't suspect that Bruce would arrive in a pink tutu or a nurse's uniform, or whatever his peculiarity is this week.

23 FRIDAY

The Higginbottom is hanging safely in the living-room. It is in a lovely gilt frame which polishes up wonderfully.

24 SATURDAY

Art Appreciation Evening with Finger Buffet. Another great success, of course. The Douglas Chater turned up with Rose on his arm, which was a bit of a surprise. But when Rose saw the painting she had an even greater surprise in store. "Ooh that's me!" she cried. "Reg painted that last summer."

We have bought a portrait of my sister. 'Woman: Prone' is Rose. The vicar's wife thought it was beautiful.

1, 8, 12, 24, 34, 39. No luck again.

SUNDAY 25

Rose brought Daisy and Onslow round to look at her portrait. "How romantic," said Daisy. "To have a man paint a portrait of you".

"And in the nude, too," said Rose proudly.

I should have guessed! Any portrait of Rose was unlikely to involve many clothes. So I now have a portrait of a naked woman (prone) on my living-room wall. Richard must take it down immediately. Nobody must ever know.

AUGUST BANK HOLIDAY   MONDAY 26

Is it right to ask a man to handle his own naked sister-in-law? Then again, the only alternative is to ask somebody else to move the portrait, and that would require unnecessary explanations. Richard has taken 'Woman: Prone' up to the loft, although I had to give him advice on where it was safe to hold it.

27 TUESDAY

Mrs. Barker-Finch has asked to see our Higginbottom. Nosy woman. I have explained that it is not available for showing to the public at present.

28 WEDNESDAY

The telephone rang just after breakfast, and once again Richard dashed out saying that there was yet another sudden Council Crisis. I made him put on a tie first, aware even at moments of acute crisis of the social demands of his position as a man in early retirement.

29 THURSDAY

If Richard is a man in early retirement, why is he needed at times of Council Crisis? I must check further with Mrs. Councillor Nugent.

FRIDAY 30

Rose telephoned. Could Reg come round and look at his portrait? He wants to see it hanging in a real room.

Richard has brought 'Woman: Prone' down from the loft, although I had to give him advice on where it was safe to hold it.

SATURDAY 31

Rose and Reg Higginbottom came round to look at 'Woman: Prone'. He is a very artistic man. No tie, no socks. He drives a very old and very dirty vehicle.

"I always liked that painting", he said. "But I don't think it's quite finished yet. I had to rush it a bit for the Summer Show. Could I just add a bit?"

I said "What, here and now?" and he replied "Yes. I've got my paints in the van. Rose, take your clothes off."

I have decided we like the painting as it is. It does not need any more work on it.

1, 8, 12, 24, 34, 39. No luck again.

1 SUNDAY

Richard has taken 'Woman: Prone' up to the loft again, although I had to give him advice again on where it was safe to hold it. In future when sponsoring art, I will check rather more carefully who the artist has used as a model. Perhaps we should stick to sunsets. I do like a good sunset, and a frame that doesn't gather dust.

2 MONDAY

Richard has been out for much of the day, and he came back with the car looking very much less clean than a car parked in The Avenue ought to look. He says he has just 'been into town'.

He also says that that fine BBC television programme, 'The Antiques Road Show', is coming to our neighbourhood. He saw a poster in the Town Hall.

This is most exciting. On Saturday 28th September, Carldon Hall will be the scene of an 'Antiques Road Show'. Well, of course, I know her ladyship well, having corresponded with her for charitable purposes, so we must be there.

ANTIQUES · ROADSHOW

·BBC·

CARLDON HALL
Saturday
28th September

What pieces shall I take? There is always my Royal Worcester double-glazed Avignon china, or our hall barometer which we bought very cannily at a boot fair a few years ago.

My Royal Doulton with hand-painted periwinkles is probably too valuable to transport, even to the comparative security of Carldon Hall. The insurance company would have a fit if they thought it was being moved without good reason.

6 FRIDAY

Some of my jewellery is very good. Daisy says that Onslow's vest probably qualifies as an antique

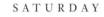

7 SATURDAY

Perhaps we ought to buy a few new antiques? When I suggested this to Richard, he was not enthusiastic. I don't think he even really wants to join in the fun and excitement of appearing on television. Of course, one does not want to hog the whole programme. That would be just too ostentatious.

1, 8, 12, 24, 34, 39. No luck again.

Our Meissen figurines? Or our genuine imitation Queen Anne corner cabinet? Richard has said he refuses to dismantle our living-room for the purposes of a television programme, but I understand Delia Wheelwright is giving her grandfather clock a facelift in preparation for the great event, so we cannot hold back on the effort required.

It must be the corner cabinet. I am also wondering about the painting of Sir Winston Churchill, as I understand the original was destroyed by Lady Churchill, which will make our print particularly valuable.

10 TUESDAY

Delia Wheelwright is hiring a van to transport her grandfather clock to Carldon Hall!

11 WEDNESDAY

After some time on the telephone (which is still not working properly: I was cut off at least twice), I have managed to secure the services of a removal company who have the Royal Warrant on the side of their vans. Our corner cabinet is virtually Queen Anne, after all.

12 THURSDAY

Richard wonders why the Royal household needs a removal company, when they've lived at the same address for generations.

I am not a superstitious person, but today has not been a good day. Richard was involved in a car crash. It seems that nobody was badly injured, but it has resulted in a scratch in the door. Richard makes light of it and refuses to tell me exactly what happened, but I will not be seen at Carldon Hall in a damaged executive class car. I think Richard needs me by his side when he goes driving in future.

Our car has gone to the garage for repair, so we cannot go to Marston Hall. It seems such a long time since we were last at our country retreat. I do so miss it, and I also need to remind myself which of our valuable antiques on display there we could show to that nice Mr Scully.

1, 8, 12, 24, 34, 39. No luck again.

15 SUNDAY

I will organise a Merrie England Barbecue for next weekend, to celebrate Britain's antiquity and discuss with our guests the many aged and valued objects that we will be presenting for the appreciation of 'Antiques Road Show' viewers at the end of the month.

Guests:

~~Reggie and Fiona Thorgunby~~ (Busy. And I couldn't last an evening with her silly squeaky voice)

~~Mr. and Mrs. Frosticles Millburn~~. (Breakfast Cereal Producers Association meeting in Abu Dhabi)

~~Porky and Mrs. Porky Hooton~~ (Golf tournament in Dagenham

Elizabeth and Emmet

The Major ~~and Mrs. Wilton-Smythe~~ (pantophobia)

~~Delia Wheelwright and that husband of hers.~~ (Mending broken grandfather clock, I expect)

~~Sir~~ Edward and partner

16 MONDAY

The next question is what to wear for the 'A.R.S', as I understand it is called in the trade. My dress sense is talked of up and down The Avenue and my hats are the envy of the Church Ladies' Circle. It will be on colour television, so perhaps the green and blue pastel silk will be best. And two rows of pearls.

TUESDAY 17

Richard will wear a suit and his regimental tie. He will visit the barber the day before the broadcast.

WEDNESDAY 18

Charity Shop Day. Rather quiet today, as it often is when I am running it. This gave me a good chance to go through everything in the shop to see if there was anything worth showing to the antiques viewing public. There wasn't.

THURSDAY 19

The car is back from the garage, no longer scratched. There is no mention in the local newspaper of the crash that caused it, so I must assume that Richard managed to hush it up through his good connections with the press.

20 FRIDAY

The telephone rang again, and after a brief conversation, Richard said he needed to go out for a short while. I insisted on coming with him, as I am sure he is in need of my help to ensure he drives safely, but he was not enthusiastic. Does he not want me to come for a drive with him? We drove round the town, bought a newspaper, and came home again. I can't see why that should be

21 SATURDAY   so important to Richard.

Marston Hall. At last we are back in our country roots. I have checked in my diary, and I see that we have not been here for two months, since just before our maritime holiday. Richard spent much of the afternoon practising for tomorrow's barbecue, as I do not want him to set fire to Sir Edward's foot.

1, 8, 12, 24, 34, 39. No luck at all.

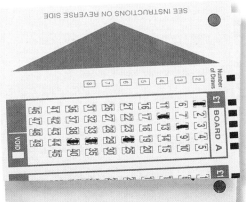

Merrie England Barbecue. Another splendid success. Sir Edward was accompanied by Rose, who had dressed in a nurse's uniform to show how hard she is working to make him feel better despite his gout. I must say he is looking a little perkier, if a little tired. It is wonderful to see my sister making such a valuable contribution to the life of our little community. The Major did suffer second degree burns to his person from backing into a plate of lamb chops, but in the circumstances I think he got off lightly. I am sure it is not good manners to refer to your hostess as 'my little minx'.

One more day at Marston Hall. I could not resist it in the glorious autumn sunshine, and anyway we had to clear up after our barbecue. Much of the ivy on the side of the building was looking rather sickly anyway, so I don't think Rose climbing up it made a great deal of difference.

24 TUESDAY

Trying on hats for the 'A.R.S.' Perhaps my Ascot hat is the one to wear, especially as it did not feature on television that day.

25 WEDNESDAY

Elizabeth came in for coffee. I did not risk my Royal Doulton, as I am sure they will be highly valued on television this weekend. The stain on the scatter rug will soon be gone. Elizabeth is coming to Carldon Hall too. She has a couple of old pieces of silver she is interested in, and a little painting which can't be worth much because it is so small.

26 THURSDAY

Richard disappeared again, without letting me come in the car with him, and came home with a hole in his shirt. Sometimes I worry about him.

Richard has had a haircut. I have finally decided on the wide-brimmed cream hat trimmed with carnations, and the van is booked for 7. a.m. We are ready.

The Antiques Road Show at Carldon Hall.
They obviously have no idea. My Queen Anne corner cabinet was dismissed as an imitation, which of course it is, but it is a _genuine_ imitation. The Royal Doulton is 'good, but common enough'. Nothing in our household is common.
But then in the middle of the show, Daddy suddenly came in on his ancient bicycle, wearing his full Army uniform and threatening everybody with his silly old rifle. Half the Hall ran for cover, but while Richard and I tried to calm him down, one of the BBC men came up and started asking Daddy about his bicycle, his rifle, his uniform and his medals. They are all very valuable.

1, 8, 12, 24, 34, 39. No luck again.

29 SUNDAY

Apparently they don't show it all on the television. They only record the best bits to make a half-hour programme. I suppose that means Daddy might not feature in the final programme. All we can do is hope.

Richard says he can't afford the insurance on Daddy's antiques, but he must. The medals and the rifle will go on display in The Avenue at once.

30 MONDAY

Daddy doesn't want his rifle and medals locked up in our Queen Anne corner cabinet. He says he needs them whenever Colonel Dawlish summons him. Such a great mind once!

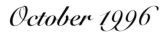

TUESDAY 1

Elizabeth came in for coffee and almond surprises, promptly this time. She seems so happy that her little picture was valued by the television people much more highly than she had expected. I did not have the heart to tell her that I did not think they really knew what they were talking about.

WEDNESDAY 2

Daisy rang. The police have been round to her house, asking whether Daddy has a licence for his rifle. Why should he need a licence? It is a valuable antique, even if the police and Sir Edward seem to think it is more of an offensive weapon than an antique.

THURSDAY 3

Daisy rang. They have had a call from the local transport museum, wanting to put Daddy's bicycle on permanent display. Daddy says he still needs it for delivering messages across enemy lines.

4 FRIDAY

Without a rifle, which the police have impounded for his own safety, Daddy is reluctant to deliver messages across enemy lines. The bicycle is going to the transport museum.

5 SATURDAY

Church Hall Bring and Buy Sale. My home-made vanilla and strawberry iced sponge cakelets sold very well. One little boy with no table manners at all spat one out all over his little sister, and his mother offered me £1 for the Crown Derby plate from which they were being served.

Delia Wheelwright asked where Richard was. Odd woman. Mock Tudor house and Mock Tudor standards, if you ask me.

Richard was out buying a lock for the corner cabinet so that we can store Daddy's antique rifle within police guidelines.

1, 8, 12, 24, 34, 39. No luck again.

SUNDAY 6

We drove out to the transport museum with Daddy's bicycle. Daddy came too, for the official handover ceremony, and Daisy, Onslow and Rose would not be left out. Daisy was wondering whether to offer Onslow's car to the curator at the same time. Rose seemed to be wondering whether to offer herself to the curator.

MONDAY 7

There was a disappointing level of press coverage at the handover ceremony. What is the point in getting Daddy dressed up if there is no photographer on hand to record the important scene? The local newspaper does not understand what news is of interest to the community, and what is not.

8 TUESDAY

I have had to place my own announcement in the local paper, giving times when Daddy's bicycle is on display. The museum do not seem to want to publicise their important new acquisition.

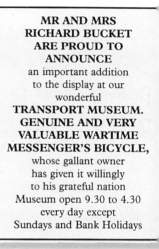

MR AND MRS RICHARD BUCKET ARE PROUD TO ANNOUNCE an important addition to the display at our wonderful **TRANSPORT MUSEUM. GENUINE AND VERY VALUABLE WARTIME MESSENGER'S BICYCLE,** whose gallant owner has given it willingly to his grateful nation Museum open 9.30 to 4.30 every day except Sundays and Bank Holidays

9 WEDNESDAY

The Major almost collided with me as I walked past The Laurels, trying out my new second best walking shoes. "Hello, my dear", he said. "While the cat's away, the mice can play."

"What do you mean, Major?" I replied. I may have been wincing a little as the shoes are smart but a bit tight.

"Your husband. Just like you and he, Mrs. Wilton-Smythe

10 THURSDAY

and I understand each other, if you know what I mean". I do not know what he means.

I'm so sorry about Richard," said Mrs Dobson when I met her at the smart handbags counter in the department store. I know Richard has not been awarded his OBE yet, but that is no cause for messages of sympathy.

FRIDAY 11

Richard went out early again, before even attempting the crossword in the newspaper. Come to think of it, he hasn't done the crossword for weeks.

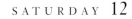

SATURDAY 12

Marston Hall. Richard seems distracted. I have asked him what is the matter, but he just says it's nothing or, this morning, "It's October." What sort of a statement is that? Of course it's October. It's October for everybody, but we don't all spend our days mooning around like a lost sheep at an auction.

If this is Richard's mid-life crisis, he should get it over and done with. There's a limit to how long a crisis can last and still be in good taste.

1, 8, 12, 24, 34, 39. No luck again.

13 SUNDAY

What Richard needs to cheer him up is an evening's entertaining. We also need to display Daddy's rifle in its new place of honour in our corner cabinet, so I have decided to host a Regimental Dinner with Full Military Honours. The Major can be guest of honour, and although Daddy's rifle will be there, I regret that Daddy himself will be confined to barracks, under sedation.

Richard's raincoat is a little crumpled. Send to cleaners?

14 MONDAY

Guests:

~~Reggie + Fiona Thorgunby~~ (Busy. And her voice is not very military. is

~~Mr. + Mrs. Frostides Millburn.~~ (Inspecting the wheat crop in the Caucase

~~Porky + Mrs. Porky Hooton~~ (Golf driving range in Walsall)

Elizabeth and Emmet (to accompany me in 'Annie Get Your Gu

The Major ~~and Mrs Wilton-Smythe~~ (ballistophobia)

~~The Commander and his good lady~~ (Sailing around the Hor

The vicar and his young wife (Onward Christian Soldiers!)

I need time to prepare for this splendid evening. Emmet and I must rehearse the songs we will perform, and I must look up a few regimental recipes.

Charity Shop Day.

Mrs. Councillor Nugent was helping me, wearing that extremely stern grey outfit she wears when she wants to scare the town clerk. The shop was empty for most of the day, and Mrs. Councillor Nugent remarked that I must be used to being on my own now.

"But I am not on my own," I replied. "I have Richard at home now that he has opted for early retirement."

"Yes," she replied, in that voice that can quell a poll tax riot, "I saw your husband

the other day. Talking to a young lady in a bus shelter."

She must have the wrong person. Richard knows no young ladies and certainly would never go near a bus shelter.

I mentioned to Richard about Mrs. Councillor Nugent and the bus shelter. He said he did not use the bus, he drives the car. Then he went back to dead-heading the roses.

18 FRIDAY

I have contacted the social columns of the local paper, and I believe they will send a photographer to be present at the unveiling of Daddy's rifle. That's what I think they said before we were cut off.

19 SATURDAY

Marston Hall. A final weekend to prepare for the unveiling. Richard is still distracted by something. He did not even put on a tie to come down to breakfast, and would have set off to Marston Hall without packing his brogues if I had not reminded him of what is expected of us in our rural hideaway.

"If it's a hideaway, nobody will see us, so it doesn't matter." He does not understand. Appearances must be kept up even when you do not make an appearance.

1, 8, 12, 24, 34, 39. No luck again.

I tried out some military food on Richard, but he did not seem very keen on them. "Just make sure there is plenty of port" is all he said. Will the vicar approve of an alcoholically fortified military evening? His young wife will.

Any more rain and I shall have to extend my weatherproof hat collection.

Rain. A dismal day. I do not seem to be as enthusiastic as once I was. But life goes on, as full of obligations as ever, so I cannot let myself slow down.

22 TUESDAY

I suppose Violet and Bruce want an invitation to the great unveiling. I'd love to be able to invite them, but you can be sure that whatever Bruce would be wearing, it would be most unmilitary. Unless he dressed as a Wren, of course, which he sometimes does.

23 WEDNESDAY

Sheridan telephoned. He is in England at the moment, in Sainsbury's to be precise. He wanted to know what that secret ingredient is that I add to my tossed green salads that makes them famous in two counties. The answer is rhythm, that's all. A musical heritage is essential in tossing a salad.

He also said he needed £50 to pay his bill at the checkout, but as Richard was out at the time, I could

24 THURSDAY
not give him his father's credit card number.

Bruce has offered me use of a regimental goat mascot that he has recently got hold of. Room for a pony and he buys a goat!

FRIDAY 25

Emmet cannot accompany me in selections from "Annie Get Your Gun". He has sprained his fingers (probably wiping up some mug of coffee spilled by dear Elizabeth) and in his words "can't even play Chopsticks". Lucky we are not eating with them, then.

SATURDAY 26

Regimental Dinner With Full Military Honours. A great success. The food was delicious, my new green evening dress with military shoulder pads and buttons on the cuffs was exactly right for the evening, and the vicar loved Daddy's rifle. The evening was a little spoilt by Richard not even being here until the hand-thrown after dinner mints were being passed round, and then he appeared in a state of some disrepair, and seized the port decanter from the Major. Unfortunately, the local newspaper photographer chose to come to the house at exactly the same time.

1, 8, 12, 24, 34, 39. No luck again.

27 SUNDAY

It may well be better if we do not have the publicity for the unveiling that I had originally hoped for. It is very ostentatious, after all, to have one's achievements trumpeted in the local paper, and I have never been one for ostentation. The photograph of Richard falling into the vicar's arms will not give the right impression, and the one of him waving Daddy's rifle at the remains of the boiled beef and carrots is just not newsworthy.

But where was Richard yesterday afternoon and evening? I haven't been able to wake him up yet to find out.

28 MONDAY

Richard has a dreadful headache. I do not care.

TUESDAY 29

Church Cleaning. Everybody seemed very distant. Mrs. Andrews smiled and said to Mrs. Barrett, "Poor woman". Mrs. Dawson smiled and said, "Never mind". Miss Barber, who usually never speaks unless spoken to, told me that she had never thought marriage was a safe thing to do, anyway. What are they talking about?

WEDNESDAY 30

The local newspaper has done its worst. Richard is described as a 'bon viveur'. In all the years we have been married, Richard has never even thought about being a 'bon viveur', and I will not have the local press casting aspersions on our integrity now. My outfit is not even mentioned.

THURSDAY 31

Elizabeth came round for a cup of nut-roasted Kenyan coffee from the lee of Mount Kilimanjaro. We did not discuss rifles, port or husbands.

1 FRIDAY

I sent Richard out to the local newsagent to buy all the remaining copies of the local paper, as there is no need to publicise some-thing as personal as a private dinner party. He returned several hours later, saying that all copies were sold out.

2 SATURDAY

The postman brought a strange letter this morning. It was addressed to Richard, the envelope was pink and it smelt of the sort of scent that Rose would wear. It had the letters S.W.A.L.K. written on the back of the envelope, which Richard says stands for Save Wallabies And Little Kangaroos. Apparently the local wild animal park is participating in a publi-city campaign.

1, 8, 12, 24, 34, 39. No luck again.

SUNDAY 3

The vicar chose to use his sermon time to regale us with his thoughts on family life for twenty-four minutes; a little too long, I fear. He told us of the place the virtuous mother holds in the family and the community - caring for her children and protecting her home and her social values without thought of any reward other than the respect of her friends and the love of her family - but he never once mentioned how important it is to tell people all the time how well one's children are doing and how happy one's husband is, to advertise the joys of a happy family home, so to speak. The vicar, bless him, has no children, and with that rather nervous wife of his it is probably better that way.

MONDAY 4

What do I do now? The only person I can confide in is my diary. I cannot talk to Daisy or Rose or Violet or Daddy or least of all Richard. How could this happen to me? But it must be true.

I have received a letter from the Ladies' Luncheon Club, informing me that 'in view of my circumstances, my membership of the Club must

5   TUESDAY

be reassessed.' It goes on, 'As you will be aware
it has always been the policy of the Club to
insist upon the highest standards among its
members, and in view of the fact that your
husband has been seen consorting with other
women, we must ask you to attend a full
committee meeting of the Club, to explain your
position.'

6   WEDNESDAY

If there is one member of that pretentious club who has always insisted upon
the highest standards, it is me (or is it, it is I?).
Just look at Delia Wheelwright's shell suits or
the way Mrs. Barrett holds her fork and ask
again who insists upon the highest standards.
But what do they mean, 'your husband
has been seen consorting with other women'?
Richard would not do that. Richard and I
are married. He is out at the moment, so I
cannot ask him, but he is not consorting
with other women. Of course he isn't.

While Richard has been out, I have been rereading some of the entries in my diary. I can now see that Richard has been acting strangely all year. It has, in the words of Her Majesty, been an annus horribilis. In March, he bought himself a new tweed jacket for no apparent reason, and within two weeks I found roses in the pockets. In July, he once went out wearing grey socks and came back wearing navy blue ones. They were both elegant pairs, which made him look as dapper as he usually does, but they were not the same pair! What can persuade a man to take off his socks and replace them with different ones while out for a morning's shopping? Could it really be another woman?

I note that on September 26th, Richard went out on an unexplained mission and returned with a hole in his shirt. At the time I accepted his explanation that it was a cigarette

10 SUNDAY

burn, although I do not know of any of his acquaintances who smoke. Could it have happened at the bus shelter?

Then what about Richard's car crash, about which he told me virtually nothing? He has been slipping out after receiving strange telephone calls, of a type which clearly should not come through on such an elegant device as our hall telephone, and he has been seen in bus shelters with strange women. In a bus shelter! How can Richard do that? Buckets do not associate themselves with bus shelters

12

Happy in their own special way.

13

It is true.
I am sure
it is true. The
evidence is all there. Little did I
realise when I began this diary that
I would be recording the end of years
of happiness. What will I tell Sheridan?
He is a sensitive little boy, and it will
do him no good at all to come from a
broken home all of a sudden. What
will I tell Daisy? Her home is about
as broken as it is possible for one to be
without actually falling down, but
she and Onslow are happy. They really
are.

THURSDAY 14

15 FRIDAY

And Rose? Maybe she has been right not to get married. She knows that all men are faithless ogres whose only pleasure is breaking hearts, but I would never have suspected my Richard of being as bad as Boris or Mr. Hepplewhite. Even Violet and Bruce are happy in their

16 SATURDAY

own way. I am not certain that I could live with a man who shares my wardrobe, which is possibly the only sin that Richard has not committed over the past few weeks, but at least they are sharing something. Richard and I have not shared anything for months, apart from a sense of foreboding when the Major arrives at one of our Candle Light Suppers without his wife.

And what can I say to Elizabeth and Emmet? I know Emmet has gone through a messy divorce and Elizabeth has a

marriage with such a large chink in it, you can see her husband's never coming back from the Middle East, but Richard and I have always been happy. We have been the rock of normality in their otherwise ravaged lives, and it breaks my heart that something as fundamental to them as the cheery morning greetings from their dear neighbours is about to change. Our morning greetings will be cheery no more. My merry trilling to Emmet will be muted.

But who is the new woman in my husband's life? Mrs. Fortescue is far too old, although her sister is married to a baronet, which makes her almost aristocracy, and thus the type of person it would be fitting for Richard to be dallying with. Could it be Mrs. Councillor Nugent? Is that the true nature of the Council Crisis?

19 TUESDAY

I know that Richard's work was always very important to the smooth running of local government, but as far as I am aware, he was never close to Mrs. Councillor Nugent. For that matter, I don't think Mr. Councillor Nugent was ever close to Mrs. Councillor Nugent.

20 WEDNESDAY

21 THURSDAY

No, I don't care what Richard is up to. It doesn't matter who the mystery woman at the bus shelter is, and I will not ask where Richard has been going when he says he is off on council business. I must keep up appearances. The leaves will fall from the trees, and my heart will break, but my rows of pearls will shine as bright as ever, and my hats will still be the talk of The Avenue. Perhaps I will hum the 'Dead March' from 'Saul' rather than the 'Deadwood Stage' but my singing will still be part of Emmet's life. Nobody will know, not even Richard, and the Ladies' Luncheon Club can expect a frosty answer. I will go out now to have my hair done. That always makes me feel better.

24   SUNDAY

25   MONDAY

TUESDAY 26

Richard's birthday. I gave him six pairs of grey socks and six pairs of navy socks. He was suitably grateful.

WEDNESDAY 27

Dates to remember
My birthday: 4th December
Our wedding anniversary
16th December
Christmas Eve Family
Dinner. 7.30 for 8

THURSDAY 28

29 FRIDAY

As if we did not have enough troubles of our own, Daisy rang to say that Daddy and Mrs. Clayton are getting married. I will not have my father taken advantage of by Mrs. Clayton. He does not belong in the Clayton family, he belongs in ours. And marriage is not a state to be recommended. Can Rose talk him out of it?

30 SATURDAY

I told Richard we must go round to Daisy's house at once.

"But I'm not wearing a tie," said Richard.

"Well, go and put one on." I will not have any nonsense from Richard, even in times of crisis.

When we arrived, Onslow was not wearing a tie. Or a shirt. The dog was still barking in the remains of their car. But there was some good news after so many weeks of unhappiness. Mrs Clayton now says she will not marry Daddy. She says she did not say she would 'marry him today'. She claims she merely offered to 'carry his tray', and he needs new batteries in his hearing aid. Daddy does not use a hearing aid. Daddy retains full use of all his faculties, at least until the pills take effect, which fortunately they have done today.

1, 8, 12, 24, 34, 39. No luck again.

I would consider asking Richard to investigate the possibilities of suing Mrs. Clayton for toying with an old man's dreams, not to mention breach of contract, but that is not the way we do things in our family. And I do not want Richard talking to lawyers at this particular juncture.

If only all family crises could be solved so quickly.

It is now only a few weeks until Christmas. Michael our postman has already been seen with a larger bag to hold all the Christmas cards which will be delivered to The Avenue, so I must begin sending ours out.

It was a difficult decision this year to decide which charity to support in buying our cards. Perhaps one concerned with the elderly, in view of Daddy's age-related difficulties? Perhaps something to do with education, in honour of our gifted Sheridan at his Polytechnic, or maybe an organisation

which deals in restoring ancient buildings, such as the one that Daisy and Onslow inhabit. But I do not want to think about broken homes at the moment.

Our Christmas cards have arrived. I have bought 200, which I hope will be enough. They are from the Landed Gentry Society, of which we are now a part.

3 TUESDAY

A day spent writing cards, both for myself and on behalf of others. It is important that we continue to be seen as the social leaders in The Avenue, whatever else is happening in our lives, and the means receiving the most Christmas cards, all with first-class stamps and envelopes.

4 WEDNESDAY

My birthday. I am not sure what to expect. I certainly do not feel like celebrating.

Well, I KNEW it!!!

I KNEW Richard's

5 THURSDAY

mid-life crisis would work out well in the end. What a day it has been.

When I awoke, Richard was sitting by the bed with a full

breakfast tray (Frosticles, toast with royally approved marmalade and Earl Grey tea and a single red rose) and a little package bearing the message "Happy Birthday". His present was wonderful – a little antique brooch with valuation and provenance, just perfect for the next time the 'Antiques Road Show' comes to town.

And his card said, 'To my dear wife, with love.' Just a simple message, but the kiss on the cheek that accompanied it told me that he meant it. I was so full of emotion that I will confess between the pages of this secret record that I shed a little tear.

"Oh Richard," I cried. "Don't run off with Mrs. Councillor Nugent! Please stay with me."

Richard looked not just shocked, he looked horrified. His lovely face drained of all its colour and his moustache looked positively limp.

He protested "Mrs. Councillor Nugent? Heaven forbid!"

And I could keep my feelings in no longer. I poured out to him my anxieties (which never deepened into suspicions, of course) about his escapades with strange women in bus shelters

8 SUNDAY

and unscheduled changes of socks. But his reply was so obvious, I am astonished I did not realise it myself.

"It's your father," he said. "I've been trying to keep it from you, but with the Mrs. Clayton business, I suppose you have a right to know. His pills have not been working very well this year. Onslow and I have been trying to keep him under control, but it has taken rather more time than I expected. The change of socks became necessary after I helped Onslow fish him out of the canal as he chased Mrs. Clayton along the towpath. Onslow needed a change of shirt and trousers."

"Well, at least there is some good in every misfortune," I said. And that was not all. It seems that the sweet smelling letters were from Daddy to Mrs. Clayton, doused in Rose's thickest perfume as were the roses in his pockets. Onslow and Richard managed to persuade Daddy that Richard would be the best go-between for the letters, but of course he did not actually deliver any of them. The lady in the bus shelter was Mrs. Clayton's daughter! As Richard explained, "We had to let her know what was going on in

your father's mind, what's left of it…"(It was a great mind in its day. Most respected in local cribbage circles).

"And the day I came home with a hole in my shirt was when Daddy shot me with his rifle", said Richard. "He and Colonel Dawlish were deep behind enemy lines at the time, so I couldn't blame him".

"Oh you poor brave thing," I said.

"The scratch on the car was when Daddy collided with it. I was parked outside Daisy and Onslow's house at the time, and Daddy came back from patrol on his bicycle. He was not in full control of his handlebars at the time".

To think I might have doubted Richard. And the new pills are definitely working. When dropped into a pint of beer, as Daddy had

rather wickedly done to Richard on the day of our Regimental Dinner, they rapidly induce an inebriated state, but when taken correctly, they now seem to be keeping dear Daddy at peace with himself, and with all who know him and love him.

13 FRIDAY

We now have sixty-three cards. This is rather more than the Hislops at number 43.

14 SATURDAY

We won the Lottery! It may be only £10, but this is the start of great things, I am sure. Sheridan rang just after the numbers were drawn, and asked for £100 which he needs to finance a new Workers' Revolutionary Macramé Co-operative. Given our new-found wealth, I could not allow Richard to refuse.

SUNDAY 15

Tomorrow is our wedding anniversary. What a lovely day that was! I remember it as clearly today as ever. That dashing slim young man who swept me off my feet and into his Hillman for a wonderful honeymoon in Weston-Super-Mare is still my consort. How lucky I am.

Sheridan's Mummy Kissing Santa Claus.

MONDAY 16

Wedding Anniversary.
Richard has excelled himself. Without any fuss at all (a characteristic which has rubbed off on me over the years, I like to think), he organised a wonderful Anniversary party which ALL our friends attended! Not only Elizabeth and Emmet, not only the Major AND his lady wife (who seems to have got over her many phobias), not only

C.P. Benedict and <u>the</u> Douglas Chater, but also the Barker-Finches and Delia Wheelwright, Mr. and Mrs. Councillor Nugent, Reggie and Fiona Thorgunby, the Porky Hootons, the vicar and his lovely wife, and of course Daisy and Onslow, Rose, Violet and Bruce and even dear Daddy, who dozed peacefully on our reproduction Queen Anne Regency chaise longue throughout the evening.

18 WEDNESDAY

I wore my new Marcasite brooch with my pink two-piece and everybody drank our health with copious glasses of champagne-type carbonated dry white wine. Emmet even accompanied me on the piano as I entertained the assembled company in selections from Gilbert and Sullivan. I am so happy.

19 THURSDAY

I have telephoned all those who were at our Anniversary party, inviting them to call in over the Christmas period to partake of mulled wine and a hot mince pie. I do think that Open House is somehow more hospitable than expecting people to arrive at a fixed time.

Another twelve Christmas cards, including one from the Wilkinsons who write 'Merry Xmas'. I cannot abide people who put 'Merry Xmas' on their greeting cards.

I will try to persuade Richard to become involved in bell-ringing next year. It will keep him fit.

I have telephoned the vicar. He is happy to have Richard as a bell-ringer. He asked if Richard is musical! How could a man with whom I have shared my life for so long be anything other than musical?

22 SUNDAY

Richard seems very keen on the idea of becoming a bell-ringer. He says there are practices two nights every week, which may take up rather a lot of his time, but if it is what I want and for the good of the church, he will give up those precious hours spent in my company.

He is truly a good man.

23 MONDAY

I think I have finished all my Christmas shopping. I am completely exhausted. The most difficult was Sheridan's present to me (after all he is an impoverished if brilliant student, and cannot be expected to pay all his own bills), but I have finally decided on a Royal Doulton serving dish, which will match perfectly the twelve setting place mats I am giving Richard.

CHRISTMAS EVE   TUESDAY 24

Christmas Eve Family Dinner. Onslow wore much more than usual, including a shirt, a tie and some socks. Rose wore very much the same as usual, that is to say very little. She was a little late as she had been seeing Mr. Duxbury. She takes the season of goodwill very seriously.

Daddy dozed peacefully on our reproduction Queen Anne Regency chaise longe throughout the evening.

CHRISTMAS DAY   WEDNESDAY 25

What a lovely day. Just Richard and I opening our presents in front of an open fire. I'm sure Sheridan would have telephoned but I understand he and Tarquin are rebuilding Bulgaria (which apparently is in need of repair) over the festive season.

BOXING DAY - HOLIDAY   THURSDAY 26

A quiet day spent relaxing and trying out Richard's place mats and my new dish on our dining table. They look wonderful. I must have my first Candle Light Supper of 1996 next week.

27 FRIDAY

I have been rereading dear Sheridan's Book Of Nursery Rhymes. How apt they are for us all this past year.

28 SATURDAY

Ride a cock horse to Banbury Cross
To see a fine lady upon a white horse
　　　(that's me, not on a horse, of course)
With rings on her fingers and bells on her toes
She shall have music wherever she goes
(especially with Emmet accompanying me on the piano)

Georgie Porgy, pudding and pie
Kissed the girls and made them cry.
(Poor Daddy, but the pills are still working)

SUNDAY 29

'My face is my fortune, sir,' she said
'Then I can't marry you, my pretty maid.'
'Nobody asked you sir,' she said
(The story of Rose's life)

Richard says that 'You owe me five farthings
say the bells of St. Martin's' sums up his life
at the moment. But money isn't everything.

MONDAY 30

Polly put the kettle on, it's time for tea.

31 TUESDAY   NEW YEAR'S EVE

Another year ends. Another year of giving myself to the community without stint, another year of putting others first whatever the cost to myself. Another year of setting the right example to all our acquaintances. Another year of keeping up appearances.

1 WEDNESDAY   NEW YEAR'S DAY-HOLIDAY

My 'Whip Crack-Away' brings
tears to the eyes.

2 THURSD